MAN OF
THE MONITOR

MAN OF
THE MONITOR

The Story of John Ericsson

BY JEAN LEE LATHAM

Pictures by Leonard Everett Fisher

J
B
E+1

HARPER & ROW, PUBLISHERS
New York, Evanston, and London

MAN OF THE MONITOR

Copyright © *1962 by* Jean Lee Latham

Printed in the United States of America

Library of Congress catalog card number: 62-8037

MAN OF
THE MONITOR

1

"Keep Your Eye on Tomorrow"

John looked across the breakfast table at his father. What was wrong? What was worrying him?

Whatever it is, John thought, I'll hear about it last. Just because I am the youngest. First, Father will tell Mother. Then they will tell Caroline. Even though she is a girl. Just because she is eleven. Then they will tell Nils. Because he is nine. He's only a year older than I am, but he'll know before I do.

Father isn't really eating his breakfast. He's just shoving things around on his plate. I wish I could say something to cheer him up!

Maybe Mr. Swenson's joke about Napoleon would make Father smile. John swallowed the last bite of his breakfast. "There! That is one thing Napoleon won't gobble up!"

Father didn't seem to hear.

Mother looked at John, smiling and shaking her head. "Where *do* you pick up such things?"

Nils answered for him. That was another thing about being youngest. The others seemed to think they could talk for you. Nils put on his grown-up air. "From old Mr. Swenson, of course. Over at Father's mine. John tags around after him all the time. Copies everything he says."

"I do not!" John yelled. He jumped to his feet, fists clenched. "I do not!" He stopped. This wasn't any time to get into a fight with Nils. Not when Father was so worried. "I'm sorry." He sat down. "It's a joke about Napoleon," he explained. "You know how people say that Napoleon has gobbled up most of Europe? And maybe he will gobble up Sweden next? Well, when Mr. Swenson is eating, he says that. 'There! That's one thing that Napoleon won't gobble!'"

He waited. Nobody laughed.

At last Father said, "I don't believe Sweden needs to worry about Napoleon, John. We've elected Bernadotte to be our next king. He was one of Napoleon's generals. That ought to save us from Napoleon."

"I was just trying to cheer you up," John said. "Because you are so worried."

Father tried to smile. "Worried? Whatever gave you that idea?"

"I can *hear* when you're worried," John told him. "It's like a machine, when some cogs are off a wheel. You know how that is? There are some little holes in the noise it ought to make."

Caroline rolled her eyes. "That child and machinery!"

John started to yell again. He clenched his teeth and counted to ten.

Mother said, "Olof, we've got to tell them."

After a moment Father said, "Yes. Time to tell them their father is a failure. I'm ruined. I'm going to lose this house, the mine—everything."

Caroline gasped and put her fingers over her mouth. She stared at Father, her eyes getting bigger and bigger.

"We haven't lost everything, Olof," Mother said. "We have each other. We have our faith in tomorrow."

"Maybe you have faith in tomorrow." Father sat with his head in his hands.

Nils asked to be excused. He went outside. Caroline began to cry. She ran upstairs.

Mother got up. "I'd better go talk to her." She followed Caroline.

John went over to stand by his father. "Will we go somewhere else to live?"

"Yes." Father's eyes looked sick. "In a turf-covered hut. And I'll grub in the fields like a peasant to keep body and soul together."

"I'll help you," John promised.

"No!" Father spoke harshly. Then he went on more quietly, "No, John. Little boys aren't supposed to have to help grown men."

"I won't always be little."

His father hugged him. Then he whispered, "Dear God, what are we going to do?"

Someone hammered on the door and called, "Mr. Ericsson?" It was Mr. Hedberg from the village.

Father got up slowly. "John, don't you want to go to the mine and tell Mr. Swenson good-by?"

"You mean you want me to clear out?"

"No, no! I . . ." Again there was that little hole between Father's words. "Mr. Swenson's going to miss you."

"Yes, sir. I'll go." John said good morning to Mr. Hedberg and raced down the road.

Mr. Swenson was standing in the door of the office of the mine. "Hello there, John! Come to spend the day with me?"

"No, sir. I just came to tell you good-by."

"But your father . . ." There were little holes in Mr. Swenson's words, too. "Why don't you spend the day? I'll show you everything. You may ask questions until you're dizzy."

"I never get dizzy asking questions."

Mr. Swenson grinned. "I've noticed that. Then you may ask questions until *I'm* dizzy."

"No, sir. I have to hurry back. I want to ask just one question. Mr. Swenson, how can I help my father? I told him I would help him, but"—John's voice shook—"it just made him mad."

4

"Now, now, John! Your father never got mad at you. I don't believe he ever got mad at anybody. You know what all the men here at the mine always say? 'Mr. Ericsson is the kindest master in Sweden.'"

"He *sounded* mad. So, how can I help him?"

"Hmmm." Mr. Swenson rubbed his chin. "If I tell you what to do, you'll remember?"

"Yes, sir!"

"Try not to yell at Nils so much."

"But I never yell at Nils unless he makes me mad!"

"I know. Try to hold your temper."

"But I never lose my temper unless people talk to me like I was little."

"You're not very big, you know."

"I'm not as little as people make me sound!"

Mr. Swenson brushed John's chin with his knuckles. "There's that lower lip, sticking out again."

John ducked his head. Then he asked, "How else can I help my father?"

"It's going to be a very different life, John. Try not to talk about how things used to be. You'll remember?"

"Yes, sir. But that is all about things to *don't*. Isn't there anything to *do*?"

"Yes. Keep your eye on tomorrow. Always!"

"Yes, sir. Keep my eye on tomorrow. I'll remember. Good-by, Mr. Swenson."

When John got home Mr. Hedberg was still there. He

5

was walking through the house with Father and writing things in a little notebook. He opened the drawer of a big chest. He whistled. "Whew! Enough silver to feed an army."

"Yes." Father spoke grimly. "I was a famous host."

"I've heard about that," Mr. Hedberg said. "Ever hear that definition of a Swede? 'A man born to have one million kronor—and to spend two million.' "

Father stood a moment, the muscles working in his jaw. "Let's get on with it, shall we?"

Mr. Hedberg opened a closet door. He touched Mother's fur cape. "I know someone who would—"

"No!" Father said. "We are allowed to keep personal belongings! She deserves something to remind her of the past."

Mr. Hedberg shrugged. They went into the library. Mr. Hedberg looked at the book-lined walls. "Enough books to educate a city! They must have cost a pretty penny."

"They did," Father said. "But I thought they were worth it." He picked up a book and smoothed the leather binding. John had never seen him look so sad.

"Mr. Hedberg, are you going to help us move things to our new house?" John asked.

"I'm going to sell things, to help your father pay his debts. You'll not be needing this sort of thing—not where you'll be living."

One open wagon, pulled by oxen, held everything they took to their new home. They started at midnight. Early the next morning they stopped.

A little wooden cottage, with a roof of shaggy turf, stood on the edge of a stony field. The doors and the wooden shutters sagged open. Dust and sand had drifted through the house. It was hard to tell where the field ended and the floor of the cottage began.

Caroline took one look and whispered, "Oh *no!*"

Mother said, "A good thing it's summertime and light so long, isn't it? Nils, you and John may gather firewood. Caroline, we'll sweep out before we begin to scrub."

That night logs crackled in the stone fireplace and firelight danced on the clean-scrubbed walls and floor. A pot bubbled on the fire.

At the supper table they bowed their heads. Silence. John glanced toward Father. He was staring straight ahead.

Mother asked the blessing. "We thank thee, God, for health and love. Be with us in our tomorrows. Amen."

Father had not moved.

Mother smiled. "Olof, doesn't this make you think of our first little home? Remember how happy we were?"

"That was different," Father said. "We were just starting out."

"That's what we're doing now," she said. "Starting all over again. We have just what we had then. Health and love and faith in tomorrow. Who knows what tomorrow may bring?"

"The winter," Father said grimly.

At first John liked the winter. He did not care if the nights were twenty hours long, and the snow drifted high as the roof. He helped make a tunnel through the snow to the shed that held their firewood and their food.

There was lots of time to sit in the firelight, carve wheels out of wood, and ask questions. Winter was all right!

Then one day he followed Mother through the tunnel to the storeroom. He looked at the shelves. "We're getting pretty low on food, aren't we?"

"John!" Mother grabbed his shoulders. "You must never say things like that! Never!"

He tried to keep his voice from shaking. "I didn't mean to make you mad."

"John dear, I'm not mad. But please, please don't say that again!" She hugged him.

John could feel her heart hammering. Mother was scared, too. She was scared about tomorrow—the tomorrow when there would be no more food.

A cold lump settled in his stomach.

2

A Special Tomorrow

One morning about a week later someone hammered on the door and called, "Hello in there!"

"It's Mr. Swenson!" John yelled. He ran to open the door.

Mr. Swenson hugged him. Then he shouted, "Good news! And here's something to help us celebrate!" He thumped a big bag on the table and began to take out food—a cooked ham, a big cheese, and loaves of bread.

"What news?" Father asked.

"Never talk when I'm hungry," Mr. Swenson declared. "I've had a long ride. Let's eat."

Mother made tea. It was very weak. John knew it was the last that they had.

After a while Mr. Swenson said, "Ever hear of the idea of digging a canal clear across Sweden? From Göteborg to Stockholm?"

9

"Of course," Father said. "Who hasn't? They've dreamed of it for hundreds of years."

"And now the dream is coming true!" Mr. Swenson said. "The Baron von Platen says we'll have a waterway coast to coast! And he's the man to do it!" He lifted his mug of tea. "Here's to the canal! The greatest engineering feat of the century! And here's to Olof Ericsson, who will help build it!"

Father's voice was husky. "You mean that? They will hire me?"

"You're already hired." Mr. Swenson tossed a little purse on the table. It clinked. "That's advance pay. To help with the expenses of moving to Forsvik. Like to ride to the village with me now? And get a sled fitted out for the journey?"

Everybody jumped up, laughing and cheering.

Father put his arm around Mother. "I—I haven't been very easy to get along with, have I? I don't know what I'd have done without you."

John edged closer to Mr. Swenson. "I tried to help, too," he whispered. "I *tried*."

Mr. Swenson nodded. He said, "John, how'd you like to ride to the village with us? Your last chance to ask questions!"

Suddenly Father threw back his head and laughed, just as he used to laugh in the old days. He was still chuckling when the three of them got into the sleigh.

After a while, though, he sobered. "I wonder if I'll ever earn enough money to send my boys to the university?"

"If you don't," Mr. Swenson said, "they'll get quite an education right there at the canal works."

"I suppose so." But Father sighed.

They reached the village and John went to the mine office with Mr. Swenson. "Mr. Swenson," he said again. "I *tried* to help, too."

"Did you remember everything I told you?"

"Yes, sir!"

"About not yelling at Nils?"

"Yes, sir."

"Did you always remember that?"

"Yes, sir! Always! Sometimes I remembered *before* I yelled, and sometimes I remembered *after*. But I always remembered."

Mr. Swenson chuckled. Then he said, "You're going to like it at Forsvik. More machinery than you ever saw before in all your life. You know what we're going to do on that canal? We're going to sail ships uphill and downhill, right across Sweden."

He drew a picture.

"Suppose a giant took a knife, and cut across Sweden, from east to west, right down through the hills. This is what a slice of Sweden would look like. Here, on the west coast, is Göteborg. Ships can sail to it. Here, on the east coast, is Stockholm. Ships can sail to it, too.

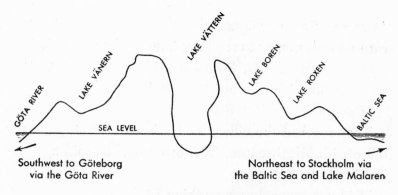

A diagrammatical cross section of Sweden

But in between Göteborg and Stockholm, there are hills.

"High up here, in the hills, are some big lakes. Suppose we wanted to sail a ship down from one of these lakes to Stockholm. We'll cut steps in the sides of the hills. We'll build a huge box, or tank, in each step. We call those tanks 'locks,' because we can lock water in or out of them. We build gates between the tanks. We can open and shut the gates. We put holes in the bottoms of the gates, to let water in and out of the tank when the gates are closed.

"High up here, by a lake, we have the first tank. Its walls are level with the water in the lake. We open the holes in the top gate and fill the tank with water. Then we open the top gate and let the ship sail into the lock. Right now, the ship is just as high as it was when it was in the lake.

"Now we close the top gate, and the water holes. We

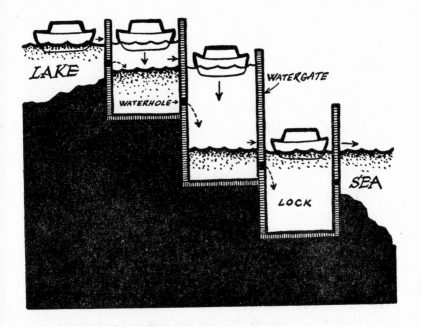

open the water holes in the bottom gate. What happens?"

"The water runs into the tank below!" John said. "The ship starts sinking!"

"That's it! Now, when the water in the first tank and the second talk is level, we open the gate between them and let the ship sail into the next lock."

"I see!" John shouted. "I see how it sails downhill! But how does it sail uphill?"

"Remember, at the top of the locks we have water—plenty of water. We can open and shut the water holes, and let water into any of the locks.

"Suppose we have a ship in this bottom lock, five

steps down from the lake up here. We close the gates. We begin to run more water into this lock. What happens to the ship?"

"It rises!"

"That's it! And when it's up high enough, we open the upper gate and sail the ship into the next lock."

"And then you close the gate, and the downstairs holes, and you run more water into that lock!" John said.

"You've got it. So that's the way we're going to sail ships uphill and downhill, right across Sweden. We'll build canals and locks to connect all the lakes and rivers."

"Will it take a good while to do it?" John asked. "Till I'm big enough to help?"

"You'll be a man grown before the canal is done."

"I wish I could work on it now," John said. "I want to do something real!"

"You've got something real to do." Mr. Swenson looked very solemn. "Listen to me, John, and don't ever forget what I'm going to say. Someday you are going to be an engineer. A great engineer."

"What does an engineer do?"

"He builds! He builds the roads, the canals, the bridges. He builds machinery, ships, and great buildings. Everything that makes life easier for people— everything—has been built by engineers! John, a great engineer is the most important man in the world! And that's what you're going to be. One of the greatest engineers in the world! So—start getting ready for it. Study! Learn!"

"What must I learn?"

"Just about everything there is. First—arithmetic. All kinds of mathematics."

"I'll like that. What else?"

"Mechanical drawing. So you can make pictures of things you are going to build."

"I don't need pictures. I see them in my head."

"If you have a lot of men working for you, they will need pictures to know what to do."

"Oh . . . I see. I'll like that, too. Just so I don't have to study languages."

"Languages, too," Mr. Swenson said.

"But why?"

"Because a lot of the best engineers are from other countries."

John stared. "You mean they can't talk Swedish? But they know more than *we* do?"

Mr. Swenson nodded. "There are going to be English engineers helping us build the canal."

"Oh . . . And if I can talk English, I can ask them questions, too, can't I?"

Mr. Swenson chuckled. "That's it! The more languages, the more questions."

They heard Father outside, shouting gaily to some

men. Mr. Swenson shook hands with John. "Good-by, lad. I'll miss you. Maybe you'll write me a letter some-day?"

"Yes, sir. Especially if I start growing bigger. I'll write and tell you about that."

"There are two ways to grow, John. Inside and out-side. You take care of the growing inside, and the Lord will take care of the growing outside."

"You are sure?" John asked. "The Lord hasn't been doing much about it so far. Nils is lots bigger. But I'll write to you. I promise. On my birthday. I'll let you know how much I've grown."

31 July 1812

Dear Mr. Swenson:

I am nine today, but I don't think I am very much bigger. There is lots of machinery here. Father took me to see a sawmill. Then I made one.

I can ask a good many questions in English now. I ask Mr. Dawson questions. He is a draftsman. He makes drawings.

Your friend,

John Ericsson

John had been sitting on the high stool by Mr. Dawson's drawing board for two hours.

At last Mr. Dawson sighed. "Who taught you so much English?"

"You did, Mr. Dawson!"

"I wonder what happened when I was a baby?" Mr. Dawson muttered. "Maybe the nurse dropped me on my head."

The door opened. A slim, quiet man came in. He wasn't dressed in uniform, but he moved like a soldier. Mr. Dawson jumped up quickly and bowed. "Baron von Platen! We are honored!"

John slid down from his stool and bowed, too.

The Baron smiled at him, then glanced around. "Don't let me interrupt your work. I was just looking for someone. I see he is not here. Do you know where I'll find John Ericsson?"

"I'm John Ericsson, sir."

The Baron smiled again and shook his head. "Not you, little fellow. I'm looking for the young man who made the model of the sawmill."

"I did it, sir."

"What? How old are you?"

"Next year I'll be ten, sir."

"And you made the sawmill yourself? Without any help?"

"Yes, sir."

"How did you make your saw?"

"With an old watch spring, sir."

"Who cut the teeth in it?"

"I did, sir. With a file."

The Baron put his hands on John's shoulders. "John

Ericsson, you keep on the way you're going, and some-day you'll do something great!"

"Thank you, sir."

"What are you doing now?"

"I'm learning about mechanical drawing. Mr. Dawson helps me. He answers my questions."

"Excellent!" The Baron shook Mr. Dawson's hand. "Good for you! Help him all you can, Mr. Dawson! He's worth it!"

"Yes, Baron."

After the Baron had gone, Mr. Dawson sat on his stool again. John climbed up on his stool, too.

"Yes," Mr. Dawson muttered. "The nurse dropped me on my head. What's more, I was born under an un-lucky star."

It must be a joke. John laughed, to pretend he understood.

Mr. Dawson scowled at him a moment. Then he opened a drawer and took out a drawing. "John, it's time for you to practice drawing. Take this drawing home with you. When you can make a perfect copy of it, bring it to me. Then you may ask some more questions. How's that?"

"Yes, sir," John said. "I can't make it look exactly like that. I don't have a drawing pen. And I don't have any brush to paint with."

Mr. Dawson patted his shoulder. "Good! That'll give

you something interesting to do! Figure out how to
make a drawing pen and a paintbrush! Run along now!
Come back as soon as you've made a perfect copy."

"Yes, sir. Thank you very much, sir."

"The pleasure is all mine!" Mr. Dawson said.

All afternoon John practiced on the drawing with an
ordinary pen. But he could not make the lines look
right. He had to have a drawing pen. He had to have a
pen with two points that he could press together or
spread apart.

He stopped trying to copy the picture. He thought
about paints and a paintbrush. He could make blue
paint with indigo. He could make yellow paint with
gamboge. But what about a brush? At last he had an
idea.

That night at supper he said, "Mother, I need some
hairs to make a paintbrush. If I could take some out of
your cape . . ."

Father had never sounded so stern before. "No! That
cape is the only decent thing your mother has! You'll
not touch it!"

"No, sir."

Two days later John finally figured out how to make
a drawing pen. "Mother, may I borrow your tweezers?"

"Will you be very, very careful not to lose them?"

"Yes, ma'am! I'll never lose them!"

He hurried off to his room with the tweezers. It took a long time to file the ends of the tweezers into points. But at last it was done. He made a little loop of thread to slide up and down on the tweezers. He could press the points together or spread them apart. A perfect drawing pen!

He set to work copying the drawing. At last it was done, ready to be painted. If only he had a brush. Maybe if he showed his work to Mother . . .

Mother came to his room. She looked at his drawing. "John! You did it yourself? But it's amazing! I'm so proud of you. I—" Then she gasped. "John! What happened to my tweezers?"

"I made a drawing pen of them."

"But you promised to take care of them! To—"

"You just said not to lose them, Mother. And I didn't."

After a moment she began to laugh. "Oh, John, what am I going to do with you?"

"I thought maybe—when you saw my drawing—all done but the painting—because I don't have a paintbrush—"

"You thought I'd let you jerk hairs out of my cape?"

"I'll be very careful. I won't take them in bunches. I'll pull them one at a time."

Mother brought him the cape. "Here. But, for goodness' sake, be careful!"

"Yes, ma'am!"

After a while he took the cape back to her. "Try to see where I took out a hair."

Mother carried the cape to a window. She went over it inch by inch. "Not a sign. Did you really get enough for a brush?"

"I didn't hurt it?" John asked. "You're sure?"

"Not at all. Did you get enough for a brush?"

"I got enough for six brushes."

"What!"

"Without hurting the cape, Mother! You said so yourself!"

Mother began to laugh. "What will ever become of you?"

"I'm going to make drawings," John said.

3

Bernadotte

When John had finished his copy, he took both drawings to the office. Mr. Dawson was alone.

"It certainly is quiet in here," John said.

"It's been that way for days," Mr. Dawson growled. "I thought you weren't coming back till you had made your drawing."

"Here it is."

Mr. Dawson looked from his drawing to the copy. "I said you had to do it yourself."

"I did."

"Where'd you get a drawing pen?"

"I made it. And a paintbrush, too. See?"

Mr. Dawson studied the tweezers and the brushes. "If I told you to walk from here to Finland, you'd be back in a week."

John decided that was another joke. He smiled. "So now we're ready for more questions, aren't we?"

"Don't you want to learn about other jobs on the canal, John? More important things than mechanical drawing?"

"But there *isn't* anything more important than drawing!"

"Who said that?"

"You did, Mr. Dawson. When you first came. Remember? I asked you who was doing the most important job around here?"

"*Pride goeth before a fall,*" Mr. Dawson growled.

The door opened and a stranger came in. He was a tall young man with light hair and gray eyes. He saw John and his eyes crinkled at the corners.

"I'm John Ericsson," John told him. "I speak English a little."

"I'm Charles Wallace," the young man said. "And I speak Swedish a little."

Mr. Dawson jumped up. He beamed. He slapped Mr. Wallace on the shoulder. "You're just the man I'm looking for! Tell John who's doing the most important work around this canal!"

"I am, of course." Mr. Wallace grinned. "I'm the new leveler."

"You measure where the men are to dig the steps up and down the hills?" John asked.

Mr. Wallace's eyebrows went up. "Say, how did you learn so much about this work?"

"I ask questions. Don't I, Mr. Dawson?"

For a moment Mr. Dawson's smile got stiff. Then he smiled more than ever. "That's it, Wallace! He's a wonderful little friend. Never meddles with anything! Just asks questions! I've told him all I can about mechanical drawing. Now he ought to be learning about something more important."

"Fine! Come along with me, John," Mr. Wallace said.

"You won't feel bad about it, Mr. Dawson?" John asked.

"The pleasure is all mine," Mr. Dawson said. "I mean," he added quickly, "I want you to learn everything you can."

John shook hands and followed his new friend out of the office.

31 July 1813

Dear Mr. Swenson:

I am ten today, but Nils is still a lot taller. I am printing this, so you can see how well I am getting along with mechanical drawing.

I have a good friend named Charles Wallace. He is a leveler. He lets me look through his theodolite. It is like a spyglass on three legs.

Your friend,

John Ericsson

31 July 1814

Dear Mr. Swenson:

I am eleven today, but I'm not growing very fast

yet. Last winter I made some drawings for the work on the canal.

My friend Mr. Wallace says I will make a good leveler when I get taller. Now, I have to stand on a stool to see through the eyepiece.

Your friend,

John Ericsson

31 July 1815

Dear Mr. Swenson:

I am twelve today, but not any taller than I was yesterday when I was eleven. (That is a joke.)

Do you remember our joke about Napoleon when I was a little boy? About what Napoleon wouldn't gobble up? Now the English have gobbled up Napoleon.

I'm making drawings for the archives of the canal company now. If I'd just get taller, I could be a leveler in the summer and make drawings in the winter.

Your friend,

John Ericsson

31 July 1816

Dear Mr. Swenson:

I am thirteen today. I am a leveler this summer, even though I am not tall enough. I have a man to carry a stool for me to stand on. My friend Mr. Wallace has gone back to England. I miss him but I like my job. I have six hundred men working under me.

Tomorrow is going to be the most exciting day in my life. Baron von Platen is going to bring Prince Bernadotte and the Prince's son Oscar to see our work.

Your friend,

John Ericsson

After supper that evening John went out into the forest, far enough from the house so that nobody could hear him. He pulled a paper from his pocket. What a surprise he had for Prince Bernadotte! A speech in French! It had been hard enough to write it, having to look up so many words. Then it seemed even harder to memorize it. But what a nice surprise for Bernadotte.

Funny . . . someday the Prince would be King of Sweden
. . . but he could not talk Swedish.

John read through his speech twice, then folded the
paper, stood at attention, and recited:

"Welcome, Your Highness! And behold, Your Highness, how the wheel of fortune turns! Six years ago
Napoleon was the greatest man in Europe. And you
were just one of his generals. You know why we elected
you Crown Prince, don't you? Just to keep on the good
side of Napoleon.

"Behold how the wheel of fortune turns! Napoleon is
a prisoner and you are a prince!"

That night he went to sleep whispering, "Behold how
the wheel of fortune turns!" The next morning he
walked to where they were digging, whispering, "Welcome, Your Highness!"

The captain in charge came over to speak to the men.
"Some of you may remember we are going to have visitors today." Laughter swept over the men. The captain
smiled. "I see you do." Then he stopped smiling. "Just
one thing! And this is an order! Prince Bernadotte has
asked that you do not stop work and stand at attention
if you see him. He says he wants to see the job in operation. Is that understood?"

John saluted. "One question, sir?"

"Yes, Ericsson?"

"If Prince Bernadotte should—uh—speak to a man—

uh—then you would have to stand at attention, wouldn't you?"

The captain's lips twitched. "Yes, Ericsson. You have my permission to stand at attention—if Prince Bernadotte speaks to you."

Behind John, a workman whispered, "Think the Prince will be able to see our Little Leveler?"

The whisper spread, and a muffled chuckle spread with it. The captain did not seem to notice. He wheeled and strode away.

Old Alex Nilsson shouldered John's theodolite and picked up his stool. "Ready, Mr. Ericsson, sir?"

John nodded and stalked off.

A workman said, "Ready, Your Honor?" He said it just loudly enough so that John could pretend not to hear it.

John clenched his teeth. When I'm bigger, he thought, just let one of them say, "Your Honor." I'll whip around, and I'll yell . . . He didn't dare yell at them now. His voice was changing.

But, he thought, when I grow *up* and my voice stays *down*, they'd better watch out!

Old Alex stopped and set up the theodolite. "Ready, Mr. Ericsson, sir?"

John forgot his anger in his work—and in thoughts of his speech. All morning one sentence ran through his head: "Behold, Your Highness, how the wheel of fortune turns!"

It was mid-afternoon when John heard the captain's voice behind him. "Ericsson!"

He froze. Prince Bernadotte was going to speak to him. His mind went blank. His speech! How did it begin? He wheeled about on his stool, snapped to attention, lost his balance, flailed the air, and sprawled at Bernadotte's feet.

He heard the laughter. It began with the captain and the visitors. It spread in waves across the mob of workmen. If only he could sink into the ground and never come up again!

A young man, still laughing, was picking him up and dusting him off. "I'm Oscar," he said in Swedish. "My father wanted to see you."

John stiffened to attention again and faced Prince Bernadotte. He felt a prickle go down his spine. What a king Bernadotte would be! Tall, dark, and fiercely handsome!

Oscar looked like his father, only not fierce. He spoke to John again in Swedish. "Are you truly the John Ericsson who made the charts in the office?"

How should he speak to the Prince's son? "Yes, Your Highness."

Oscar spoke to his father in French. Bernadotte glared at John and turned to the Baron, shouting and waving his hands.

"I'm sorry I made him mad!" John whispered.

"He's not angry! That's just his way," Oscar said. "He is saying you are magnificent. Unbelievable."

Why, oh, why couldn't he remember his speech? Maybe if he went on talking he would think of it. "You speak Swedish very well, Your Highness."

Oscar smiled. "Why not? It is the language of the country I love."

"Does your mother, the Crown Princess, love Sweden, too?" John asked.

Suddenly something was wrong. Oscar stopped smiling. The captain and Baron von Platen glared at John. Only Prince Bernadotte was still talking. The Prince turned to John, grabbed his shoulders, and kissed him on both cheeks. He rattled off another volley of French. He marched away. The others, still grim-faced, followed him. John stared after them, bewildered. What had he done?

An hour later the captain sent for John. The visitors had gone. The captain was alone. He still looked grim. "Ericsson, why in heaven's name did you ask about the Crown Princess?"

"I—I—was just trying to be polite."

"You could not have said anything to hurt Bernadotte's son more deeply. Prince Bernadotte's wife is not with him. She went back to France."

"She doesn't love her husband?"

"She loves him and he loves her. But—well, she couldn't get used to Sweden. Everything was too strange. She was too lonely."

"But what about Prince Bernadotte? Isn't he lonely?"

"He has his work, Ericsson. That's what a man does when he's lonely. He works like the devil."

"Yes, sir. I'm sorry, sir."

"That's all, Ericsson. Dismissed."

John gulped. "You mean . . . from my job?"

"What? Never! You know, Ericsson, someday you are going to be a great engineer."

No, I am not going to be an engineer. John thought it, but he did not say it. He only said, "Thank you, sir," and marched out of the office.

No, not an engineer. Someday, when he was big enough, he knew what he would do. It was no use to tell anybody about it now. Not until he was big enough. Then he would tell them. He would tell Father and Mother and Mr. Swenson. He would say, "I am going to be a soldier—like Bernadotte!"

4

"Admiral of the Rafts"

In 1818, when John was fifteen, news came from Stockholm: Charles XIII was dead. Bernadotte was now Charles XIV John of Sweden.

The officers on the canal work toasted their new king. They retold stories of his great battles.

"If anyone can save Sweden from her enemies," one officer said, "he is the man! Long live Charles John!"

Someday, John thought, *when I'm big enough . . .* If only he would grow faster!

Two years later, when he was seventeen, he decided the time had come to join the army. He was not tall—not quite five-feet-eight—he had given up hope of growing taller. But he was strong. Now was the time to tell them . . . There was only Mother left to tell. Both Father and Mr. Swenson were dead.

John remembered his last talk with Father—how

Father had said, "I'm sorry I couldn't do more for my sons. Give you the education you deserve. But you'll both succeed in spite of that. You'll both be great engineers."

He remembered his last letter from Mr. Swenson: "You're living up to what I said about you, lad. You're going to be a great engineer."

If they were alive now, I'd make them understand, John told himself. He went to talk to his mother.

She listened. For a long time she was silent. At last she asked, "You're sure that's what you want?"

"More than anything in the world!"

Silence. At last she said, "I was thinking of when you were a little boy. You'd be building something. I'd call you to supper. You'd say, 'I'm coming, Mother,' and go right on working."

John grinned. "I've been a nuisance, haven't I?"

"And sometimes, even when you weren't building something—when you were just thinking about it—it was the same way. You'd say, 'I'm coming, Mother,' and never stir."

John chuckled. "You've had the patience of Job."

Her eyes were troubled. "What will happen in the army, John? If you get to thinking and don't hear an order? Do you think your officers will have the patience of Job? John, dear, are you *sure* it's what you want?"

"More than anything in the world!" he said again.

"Then you'll go with my blessing." She smiled. "You'd go anyway. . . . Have you told the Baron von Platen?"

"Er . . . no. I guess . . . I didn't think of that."

"Or thought you'd join before you told him?"

John grinned again. "Maybe. Might be a good idea. Then there wouldn't be anything left to say."

But he found the Baron von Platen had plenty to say. "You idiot! You fool! You in the army? It's a criminal waste of brains! You . . . Oh, go to the devil!"

John saluted and went to join his regiment. The Baron will change his mind when he sees the kind of soldier I make! When I . . .

With his first day's drill he found he was a bewildered bungler, trying to right face, left face, and present arms when orders came so fast they tripped over one another.

That evening he sat on his bunk, head in his hands, trying to collect his wits.

Someone stopped in front of him. "Tired, eh?"

John answered without looking up. "No, not tired. Just disgusted."

"Stand at attention when an officer speaks to you!"

John scrambled to his feet and saluted the lieutenant.

"Eyes front! Get that chin in! Straighten up!"

John obeyed.

"So you're disgusted? Why?"

"I joined the army to learn to fight, sir. To—"

"And what do you think an army is?"

"A soldier is—" John began.

"I didn't ask what a soldier is. What do you think an army is? You don't know, do you? An army is a machine! A good regiment is a superbly trained machine! And a soldier is just a cog in that machine. A cog that fits in a certain place. And he is drilled until he knows that place!"

"Yes, sir."

"Until men are trained, they are not an army. We might have five hundred marksmen here. But until they are trained, they would not be an army. They would just be a mob. What would happen if they went into battle without being molded into a machine? They'd probably shoot each other! You understand?"

"Yes, sir."

"I suppose you dream of standing out someday? Well, before you can stand out, you'll have to fit in. You'll have to be a good cog! Say it! 'I must be a good cog.'"

And John, who had commanded six hundred men when he was thirteen, said, "'I must be a good cog.'"

He learned to be a good cog. He learned to fit in. He even began to stand out. He made a record on the rifle range. A gymnast came to train the men in running, leaping, and wrestling. John made a record there, too.

Even the stern colonel of the Royal Chasseurs finally looked at him intently. "Ericsson . . . John Ericsson . . . Have I heard the Baron von Platen speak of you?"

"Possibly, sir," John said. "When my father was living, he worked on the canal."

A month later the colonel sent for John. "Ericsson! Would it interest you to know I have just received a letter from the Baron von Platen?" He began to read:

"*. . . Reports of John Ericsson's markmanship, feats of strength, and tidy appearance do not please me. It is a criminal waste of brains for him . . .*"

The colonel stopped reading. He glared. "Do you know what you've done? You've put me in the bad graces of one of the most important men in Sweden!"

"I'm sorry, sir."

"Humph. . . . Is it true that you were a leveler on the canal works when you were thirteen?"

"Yes, sir."

"That you made drawings for the archives of the canal company?"

"Yes, sir."

"Small wonder the Baron feels the way he does. Think you have brains enough to learn surveying?"

"Surveying, sir?"

The army, the colonel explained, often worked on government projects. Next summer a special detail of men would go north to do some surveying. It would be a good opportunity—for the man who qualified. In addition to his regular pay, the man would be paid by the piece for the maps he made.

"But," the colonel said, "you will have to get ready at your own expense. You'll have to spend the winter in Stockholm studying for your examination. You'll have to buy your own instruments. Well? Do you want to go to Stockholm?"

"Yes, sir. Thank you, sir!"

John was in debt when he went to Stockholm. He was even more heavily in debt when he returned. He had bought the best surveying instruments he could find. He wondered how many maps he would have to draw to get out of debt. Perhaps, with all his years of mechanical drawing . . .

After the first week of surveying the lieutenant in charge stopped by John's drawing board. "Ericsson, you are quite an asset."

"Thank you, sir."

After two weeks the lieutenant stopped by his drawing board again. "Ericsson, do you have another name besides John?"

"No, sir."

"Then I'll have to give you one. I can't carry you on my payrolls as one man, turning out the amount of work you are doing. I'm not going to be called to headquarters to try to explain you!" He stalked away.

John grinned. He'd get out of debt all right. All those years on the canal . . . He thought of the charts he'd made, of the machines he'd studied . . .

Someone shook him. "Ericsson! What's the matter with you?"

He looked up blankly into Hjalmar Lind's worried face. "Eh? Nothing. I was just thinking."

"You've sat there staring at nothing for the last two hours. When I spoke to you, you said, 'I'm coming, Mother.' "

"I was thinking about a new engine," John said. "A flame engine. It would work on hot air instead of steam. Be much more efficient."

"Why?" Lind asked.

"You know how a steam engine works?"

Lind shook his head. "Make it simple," he said.

"We have a furnace to hold the fuel and a boiler to hold the water. So—the furnace provides the heat. The heat boils the water. The water turns to steam. The steam enters the cylinder of the engine to do the work. Very inefficient. We lose heat every step of the way."

"What do you plan to do?"

"Get rid of two stages in the process. Build my fire inside the cylinder. The fire will make hot air. The hot air will do the work instead of steam. Much more efficient. Safer, too. No boilers exploding."

"Hmmm . . ." Lind was thoughtful. Then he asked, "Ericsson, what *are* you doing in the army?"

John grinned. "Right now, I'm surveying."

When they returned to winter quarters, John had enough money to pay his debts and to buy material to build a model of his flame engine. For weeks he spent all his spare time on it. The first model did not work. Neither did the second one, nor the third. By the time he was building his fourth model, he had used up the last krona of his extra pay.

If only he could win a promotion to a lieutenancy. Of course there would be extra expenses at first—new uniforms—all that sort of thing. But the extra pay would help him build half a dozen more models of his flame engine—if he needed to. And he knew he might need to do just that. He was on the right track, but the road might be long.

One night he heard that the colonel was going to Stockholm in three days. A sudden idea struck him. He searched through his lecture notes on military tactics. He found a description of one of Bernadotte's campaigns. He found a map of the terrain of the action.

By dawn the second morning he had completed the largest and most beautiful drawing he had ever made. He took it to the colonel.

"Sir, when you are in Stockholm, would you present this to the King?"

"Humph. After a lieutenancy, are you?"

"Yes, sir."

"Promotions are slow in peacetime, Ericsson. But I'll

take your map. I'll present it to the King. I'll say this: it will be a credit to the regiment!"

John saw the colonel depart for Stockholm. What would be the word when he returned? Praise from the King? Perhaps a lieutenancy? The next two weeks were as long as years. If it had not been for his work on the flame engine—fourth model—the time never would have passed.

At last the machine was ready to test. This time, John knew, he had it right! When Baron von Platen heard of this, and when the King had seen his map . . .

The flame engine—fourth model—failed. For a long time John stared at it. How long he did not know. When he touched it, the fire had gone out and the engine was cold. He muttered one word, picked it up, and slammed it against the wall.

"Ericsson!"

He wheeled and saluted the stony-faced lieutenant.

"I've wondered," the lieutenant said, "about some of the scars on these walls. Hereafter—"

The colonel's orderly approached. Ensign Ericsson would report immediately. John forgot his disappointment in the flame engine as he hurried to the office.

The colonel stared at some point over John's shoulder. He spoke stiffly. "I did not get to present your map to the King. Probably just as well that I did not. At the moment I am not in favor at court."

"I see. Thank you, sir!"

"I left it in Stockholm with someone who may get the attention of the King—when he is in a better humor."

"Thank you, sir."

John returned to the barracks to clean up the wreck of his flame engine—fourth model. How long, he wondered, before he could afford to build another one?

Two weeks later he got orders to prepare to report to Stockholm. At last! His map had reached the King!

But he found he was only one of a group of men detailed to a tour of duty on a gunboat in the Baltic. They were to be trained in the handling of the big guns on the boats.

Their first morning on the boat one of the crew asked, "Ever had sea duty, Ericsson?"

John thought of his trips on the rafts in the rivers and lakes near the canal works. Of how frightened he had been at first when the waves washed completely over the logs. He remembered how he had stood in the little pilothouse in the middle of a raft and watched the logs beneath him disappear under the waves.

Now he looked over the side of the gunboat to the water below, and laughed. "I've been much closer to the waves than you ever get!" He told of his days on the rafts.

The gunboat weighed anchor and sailed east. They passed the offshore islands and reached the open sea. Long swells hit the gunboat. A queasy feeling hit John.

He tried to fight it off. He closed his eyes. That did not help. He tried staring down at the deck, up at the sails, but nothing helped. He fled to the rail.

It was three days before he could stand up long enough to help handle one of the guns. He finished his tour of duty with a new nickname: "Admiral of the Rafts."

5

Stranded

John was glad to return to his regular quarters. At least he could do things right there! A month later he stood before his colonel in disgrace. On guard duty Ensign Ericsson had allowed a man to pass unchallenged.

"Ericsson, do you know the penalty for sleeping on guard duty?"

"Yes, sir. But, sir, I was not asleep."

"Then how did you let a man pass unchallenged?"

"I was thinking about the big guns, sir. On the boats. If we had a self-acting gunlock, sir, we could fire more quickly. We'd have fewer misfires. I was thinking of . . ."

The colonel listened. His eyes narrowed. "Yes . . . I see. An excellent idea. . . . If only we could . . ." Then he stiffened. "But, Ericsson! You are either an engineer or a soldier! Which?"

"I am a soldier, sir."

"Then, so long as you are in this regiment—"

An orderly entered. A dispatch had just arrived from the King. The messenger was waiting for an answer.

The colonel scanned the paper. His eyebrows went up. He flicked a glance toward John. "See that the messenger has some refreshment. I'll prepare my answer."

The orderly went out.

The colonel jumped to his feet. "Congratulations, Lieutenant Ericsson!"

"Sir?"

"You have your commission. You deserve it. What's more, you are to report to the King for special duty. As soon as you can get your uniforms. They are quite expensive. A good thing you earned so much being two Ericssons last summer, isn't it?"

"Yes, sir. Thank you, sir." John did not explain what had happened to his money.

Soon Lieutenant Ericsson, in a fine new uniform, wearing a handsome new sword—and up to his ears in debt—stood at attention before the King and Prince Oscar.

Prince Oscar said, "At ease, Lieutenant Ericsson. Sit down."

With a smiling Oscar to translate, the smiling King explained. "Your map is magnificent. That is why I sent for you. You will be here for some weeks—perhaps months. You are to make maps for me of all my campaigns."

John tried to look dignified, but he knew he was grinning from ear to ear. What a chance to study military maneuvers! To hear, from Bernadotte's own lips, about his campaigns!

The King showed him rough sketches and explained them. John counted the sketches. "Some weeks—perhaps months," the King had said. John knew he could finish them easily in three weeks. What should he do? Work rapidly and amaze the King? Or take his time and get to stay longer in the palace?

When he started working, the question settled itself. Soon he was turning out flawless work at his usual speed. When the maps were done, he sent word that they were ready. Then he started working on a sketch of his flame engine—fifth model.

He had not heard anyone enter until Prince Oscar spoke. John leaped to his feet and saluted.

Prince Oscar looked at the maps. "Amazing!" He picked up the sketch of the flame engine. "What's this?" He listened. "Interesting." He laid it on the stack of maps. He went out.

Smiling, John waited for the summons. Smiling, he went before the King. Then the smile stiffened on his face and faded.

The King was glaring at the sketch of the flame engine. He was talking through his teeth. John saluted.

Prince Oscar spoke in a flat voice. "At ease, Lieutenant Ericsson. His Majesty wishes me to thank you for the maps. They are excellent. His Majesty also wishes to know about this other sketch."

With Oscar to translate, John explained, and the King asked questions.

Presently the King laid aside the sketch. "What are you doing in the army?"

"I'm here to serve my country, Your Majesty! So long as the might of Russia threatens us—"

"We need our army, eh?"

"Yes, Your Majesty."

"John Ericsson, you are a fool."

John felt his temper rising. He clenched his teeth.

"What do you think it takes to win a battle?" the King asked.

At least he knew the answer to that! It had been hammered into him. "A superbly trained machine, Your Majesty."

"Bah! Suppose your 'superbly trained machine' is armed with longbows, effective at two hundred yards. How long would it last against cannon, effective at two miles?" The King shook his fist and thundered. "The first requirement for an effective fighting force is up-to-date weapons! And where do we get those weapons? From engineers!"

"Yes, Your Majesty."

"How many years have you wasted in the army?"

"I enlisted in eighteen-twenty, Your Majesty."

"You must be able to present arms magnificently."

John could feel the hot blood in his face. "Yes, Your Majesty."

The King picked up the sketch of the flame engine. "Someday you will be famous all over the world. As I said, you are a fool. When this flame engine is working, ask for leave of absence and go to England."

"Why England, Your Majesty?"

"Because the industrial revolution is developing more rapidly there. You need a country with the money and the market to develop your genius."

He got up. He smiled. He kissed John on both cheeks. And he said he never wanted to hear his name again until he heard that he was in England.

By the spring of 1826—five models later—the flame engine was working perfectly.

A friend, Lieutenant Bergland, watched it. "Now what?" he asked.

"If I had a thousand kronor," John said, "I'd go to England tomorrow."

"If you can get the leave," Bergland said, "I'll lend you the money."

"What? On what security?"

"Your brains—and your heart. That's enough for me."

There was a lump in John's throat. "I'll give you a half-interest in the engine."

Bergland laughed. "Nothing of the kind! You're a genius with machinery, but a babe in arms about money. That engine will be worth ten thousand times a thousand kronor. Do you have a friend in England who can help you arrange for a demonstration?"

"Yes." John smiled. "And he'll be delighted to know I have leave from the army."

He wrote that night to Charles Wallace. Before an answer came, he had arranged for his leave and had booked passage. He wrote again, saying what ship he would arrive on. Still no answer.

He went to Stockholm to board his ship. The city was celebrating the birth of a son to Crown Prince Oscar. John did not see Prince Oscar, but he did stand in a cheering throng one day as the King rode by—a very happy looking man. His wife was by his side. After his long years alone, she had come to Sweden to be with him. How lovely she was!

John bought a gift for the royal grandson. Rather an extravagant gift, he knew. But, after all, he had a thousand kronor. He sent it with a note to Prince Oscar—congratulations and an apology. The palace was not supposed to hear from one John Ericsson until he was in England. At least he was on his way.

He sailed. With a hollow feeling he looked back. What was he doing, leaving his homeland? What would he find in England? Just one familiar face—maybe not even that. Charles Wallace had not answered his letters.

The little ship reached the open sea. John's hollow feeling turned to something more violent. He fled to his cabin. He did not leave it till the ship was in the Thames. One good thing about seasickness, he decided. He had been too sick to worry about what would happen in England.

When he stood on the deck, searching a crowd of strange faces, the panic came back. What if Charles Wallace were not there? Then he saw him, looking just as he had looked more than ten years ago—tall, fair, quiet, with the same lines around his eyes ready to crinkle with a smile.

John waved, but Mr. Wallace's glance passed over him. When John reached his side and spoke to him, Mr. Wallace's face was politely blank.

"Yes?" Then suddenly he smiled. "John! I never would have known you!" He winced at the grip of John's fingers. "Gently! Watch that handshake! You'll be meeting engineers! They need their hands!"

He apologized for the delay; he was in Liverpool now. That was why he had not heard in time to answer the letters.

"But I have arranged for a demonstration of your engine. Next Wednesday a week. I'm sorry I can't be here that day. But we'll catch up later."

"I have six months!" John said.

"Good! Er—tell me—I don't want to be rude, but do you have enough money to tide you over?"

"Oh, yes! No trouble about that!"

"Good! I engaged quarters for you. Rather expensive, but I think first impressions are important. Sorry I had to put off the demonstration that long. It was the first day I could get John Braithwaite. I did want him to be there. Fine chap. You'll like him. And he'll like you."

Mr. Wallace saw him settled in a handsome room, gave him a list of expenses to date, and wished him luck. Then he dashed off to catch the stage to Liverpool.

Alone, John went over the figures. He converted pounds to kronor. He stared at the result appalled. By the time the demonstration was over, he would not even have return fare to Sweden. He laid down his pencil. His hands were shaking.

He spent the next days walking endlessly. He told himself that he must see the sights while he had time. He knew he was walking to try to get away from panic. At night when he tried to sleep, sometimes the panicky feeling came back.

The panicky feeling was back the day he went to the hall to get ready for the demonstration. If only Mr. Wallace could have been there with him!

A rat-faced porter shuffled in and dumped a scuttleful of coal into a large box on the platform.

"What's all that?" John asked.

"Goin' to run a hengine, ain't you, Gov'nor?"

"Yes, but—"

"Tykes 'eat to run a hengine, don't hit?"

"Yes, but I've always used wood."

"Coo! Must be from a werry backward country. We been burnin' coal for years." He shuffled toward the door. "If I fill that box, will hit be enough?"

"I could run this engine a week on what you've brought already!"

"Blimy! Why didn't they *tell* me hit was nothink but a bloomin' toy?" He went out, slamming the door.

John was setting up his engine when the door opened again. He looked up impatiently. But the man who stood there, smiling at him, was evidently one of the guests.

"Mr. Ericsson?" He came forward. "I'm John Braithwaite. I know you're busy. I'll bother you only a moment. I have another appointment this afternoon. May have to leave before the demonstration is over. I did want you to understand."

"Thank you!" The hard knot in John's stomach melted. "I'm so glad you could come."

"I wouldn't have missed it. I've heard of you since you were a lad. Charles Wallace talked of you when he came back from Sweden."

"He was very good to me."

More men came in. Mr. Braithwaite strolled off to greet them. When the crowd had gathered, John fired his engine. Then he gave a brief explanation of how it worked. He had timed that explanation exactly. He knew just when to say, "And now, gentlemen, it is ready!" He knew that as he said those words, the piston would move.

As he talked, he could feel his gaze pulled time and again toward John Braithwaite, standing near the door.

Presently he said, "And now, gentlemen, it is ready!" He stepped back. He swept a gesture toward his engine. Nothing happened. What was wrong? Men stirred. They glanced at one another. One man leaned to mutter something behind his hand to the man beside him.

Mr. Braithwaite spoke. "You have used wood before, Mr. Ericsson? Coal is a little slower at the start, but more efficient in the long run."

John nodded. He tried to say "Thank you," but his throat was dry and his tongue was thick.

Then the engine began to move. Men stopped whispering. They leaned forward to watch. They got up and came nearer. John relaxed. He had won! England was his! England—with ironworks and money and markets!

Smiling confidently, he gave them the facts and figures: the horsepower the machine developed; the amazing efficiency. He spoke of the safety factor. "This is the machine," he said, "that will make the steam engine obsolete! This is the machine that—"

He stopped. The engine was creaking. The smooth motion changed to a jerk. The creaking grew louder.

"What's the trouble?" someone asked.

"I—I—don't know," John admitted. "In all my experiments nothing like this—"

A louder creak. The engine stopped.

"Heat of the coal," someone said. "Hotter flame than wood. Too much for it."

"But with wood . . ." John began.

"Probably all right in Sweden, where you still burn wood," one said. "But we burn coal. And coal seems to have made your little engine . . . obsolete."

Someone laughed. The men moved toward the door. Some murmured polite regrets. Others glanced at their watches impatiently.

At last John looked around. The hall was empty. Had Mr. Braithwaite gone before the engine failed? Not that it made any difference. He'd hear about the failure soon enough.

John touched the engine. It was cold. He grabbed it and slammed it into the box of coal.

The porter came in, tiptoeing as though at a wake. "Wot 'ave we 'ere?" he asked.

"Trash!" John said. "Dump it!"

He walked back to his hotel, packed, paid his bill, and left. He hailed a hack. "Can you find me an inexpensive room?"

The driver looked him over and grinned. "Wot 'appened, Gov'nor? Gamble and lose?"

"Exactly. I gambled and lost."

6

Deserter!

The horse clip-clopped over cobblestones. The hoof-beats echoed the words: *Gambled and lost. Gambled and lost.*

Presently they turned into a narrow, dirty street. They turned into another, narrower and dirtier. They stopped before a grimy building. " 'Ere you are, Gov'nor. You can live 'ere a month for wot you've been spendin' a day."

John paid in advance for a week's rent. He climbed narrow stairs, found his way along a dark hall reeking of mutton, cabbage, and stale grease. He entered a cubbyhole of a room and sat on a lumpy cot.

What a fool he had been! Why had he spent so much? But he had been so sure—so sure. In six months he must win. He could not go home a failure.

What could he do? How could he get a job? What company would hire him? Every engineer in England would hear about him. John Ericsson, who had swaggered about on that platform—yes, he had swaggered, he had to admit it—who had swaggered about, telling his audience that he had made the steam engine obsolete.

If he could just experiment with other grades of iron. If he could just find something that would stand the heat of the coal. But he knew how much his experiments would cost. If only . . .

At last the gray shadows in the little room were black. He stretched out on the cot, linked his hands behind his head, and tried to think.

Morning came. Gray light filtered through the sooty window again. He got up, shaved in cold water, changed his clothes, and went down into the noisy, reeking street. He remembered the clean smell of mountains. His throat ached. He shook his head impatiently. He must not think of home. He must not let his thoughts go around. He must plan! *Plan!*

But the next Tuesday morning his thoughts were still going around in circles. Once more he shaved, dressed carefully, and went down to the street. He came face to face with Charles Wallace.

"John! I thought I'd never find you! How soon can you go with me to the Braithwaite Iron Works?"

John forgot he had not eaten. "This minute!"

They climbed into the waiting hack. The driver hailed

John as an old friend. "Ready to sit in on another game, Gov'nor?"

"Ready for anything!" John said.

"It was me wot 'elped 'im find you," the driver suggested.

"And you've been paid!" Mr. Wallace said.

The driver grinned. "Cawn't blime a chap for tryin'." He slapped the reins and they clattered off.

Mr. Braithwaite's smile was warm. "Good! You're still in England! I was afraid you had gone back to Sweden! What did you do with your flame engine?"

John could feel his face get hot. "I smashed it."

"I see. Do you often smash things?"

"When anything fails—yes," John admitted.

"That's your answer to failure?" Mr. Braithwaite chuckled. "Not a bad idea. Clears the decks for action. The flame engine isn't practicable under present conditions. So—forget it for the moment. Turn to something else. You have leave of absence from your regiment?"

"For six months. About five months, now."

"And then?"

John's smile was grim. "Before the six months were up, I thought I would be well established in the engineering world. I was going to resign from the army."

"Good enough. You may resign now, if my little proposition interests you. I am looking for a junior partner."

John could only stare at him.

"How does 'Braithwaite and Ericsson' sound?"

"But I have nothing to invest in a partnership."

"Yes, you do. Your brain. You've got the brain that planned the flame engine, and the hands that built it. We'll find plenty of work for both of them. When you come up with an idea, we can experiment. There will be the iron, the tools, and the workmen to help you. There will be money—within limits. I know how much experimenting can cost. But when we hit on something that is practicable—that has a wide market—one success will support a great many experiments. How do you feel about it?"

"Like a condemned man who has been pardoned."

"Hear! Hear!" Charles Wallace said. "Come along! You gentlemen are my guests! I want to celebrate! One engineer has been rescued from the army!"

That afternoon Mr. Braithwaite took John through the plant and introduced his workmen to the new junior partner. "From here on," he told them, "it will be Braithwaite and Ericsson."

The men muttered politely, but their eyes had reservations.

Bill Sanger seemed to be the leader of the workmen. He was a squat, broad-shouldered brute of a man, with black hair growing low on his forehead, glittering black eyes, and a bulldog jaw. He stepped forward, stretched his lips in a smile, and held out his hand. Something in the little black eyes warned John that Bill intended to crush a bone or two in the handshake.

John's grip brought a grimace to Bill's face. Smiling to himself, John turned and followed Mr. Braithwaite.

Behind him he heard Bill growl, "Blasted foreigner! Ain't we got enough men beggin' for work without bringin' in a foreigner?"

You confounded fool, John told himself. Now you've got the leader of those men against you!

He followed Mr. Braithwaite into the office.

"Now," Mr. Braithewaite said, "tell me! Do you have any other ideas milling around in your head?"

"Five dozen," John said, "but most of them are just in the 'milling around' stage."

"Have you ever thought much about marine engineering? Steamships, for instance?"

"Not about *any* kind of ships, if I can help it!"

"You get seasick, eh? I sympathize. But England is a maritime nation. All navigation is important." Mr. Braithwaite leaned forward. "If I said in public what I'm saying now, I'd be declared insane. But, someday, we'll have transatlantic steamers. That day will have to wait for more efficient boilers and engines. A steamer is tethered to her fuel supply. We have plenty of little paddle-wheel steamers on canals and in coastal trade. But no ship today could carry enough coal for a transatlantic crossing—not and have anything else on board."

"I've never toyed with the thought of crossing the Atlantic," John said. He told of his seasick time on the gunboat in the Baltic. "After I recovered from that, I did have two thoughts. One, there should be an automatic gunlock. Something to make the firing of the guns more certain."

"Good!" Mr. Braithwaite said. "And what was the other idea?"

"I was thinking of a steam warship. I didn't get very far with that idea. I just made a list of the conditions of success."

Mr. Braithwaite cocked his head alertly. " 'Conditions of success.' An interesting way to put it."

"Seems to me it's the only way to begin. Start with what must be and work toward it."

"And what are those conditions?"

"A battleship must be battleworthy. For a war steamer, we've got to get rid of her paddle wheels, and any machinery above water. And we've got to get rid of her smokestack."

"But we can't dispense with a smokestack, John. And a good tall one, at that. It's got to be tall enough to make a draft for her fires. Without that, she would be helpless."

"Exactly," John agreed. "And—let one cannon ball smash into her smokestack—and she *would* be helpless. So we've got to get rid of it."

"How?"

"I don't know—yet. And I don't know how we'll get rid of her paddle wheels, either. I just know the war steamer of the future must not have them."

Mr. Braithwaite nodded. "Keep thinking about it, John. Maybe, someday, we can get the Admiralty to foot the bill for experiments in steam navigation. Meanwhile—we can foot the bill for experiments on an automatic gunlock. And, heaven knows, the army and the navy can both use it!" He smiled. "It's good to have you here. Take your time about settling down to anything. Roam around through the plant. Get acquainted with the men. I've found it pays to have the friendly co-operation of my men."

John agreed. He thought of Bill Sanger. You confounded fool, he told himself again, you almost broke his hand!

The weeks stretched into months while he worked on the gunlock. The cost of the experiments staggered him. Designing, casting, testing . . . discarding . . . designing, casting, testing . . .

"I couldn't have afforded to develop this in a dozen years," he told Mr. Braithwaite.

"When it works," Mr. Braithwaite said, "it will pay for itself."

They drove out to the isolated spot where they were testing their gunlock on a cannon. They expended another two hundred pounds of powder. More adjustments. More firings. More powder. At last the gunlock was working perfectly.

"John, you've done it!"

"*We've* done it," John said. "Now what? A patent?"

"No, no patent. That would betray the secret to the world. I'm sure the Ordnance Department would rather keep the secret."

"Then what do we do?"

"We'll write to them. Tell them what the gunlock will do. We'll offer to demonstrate it—on one condition: if it measures up to what we guarantee, they contract to buy gunlocks from us."

"How many?"

"Well . . ." Mr. Braithwaite smiled. "We may need to expand the plant to handle production."

John's lungs felt too big for his chest.

They wrote a description of what the gunlock could do. They sent a letter to the Ordnance Department.

"How long before we'll have an answer?" John asked. "Two days? Three?"

"Two months—if we're lucky."

"What! But—but—"

"So we'll work on something else."

John spluttered, then grinned. "A good thing I have you for a balance wheel."

"The gunlock is only the beginning. A lucky beginning. It will provide money for a lot of other experimentation. And a steam boiler needs a lot of that."

"Yes. There ought to be a way to condense the steam without . . ." John strolled out of the office, forgetting his hat.

The next day he was at his drawing board.

Soon they were repeating the pattern of work they had followed on the gunlock: building, testing, discarding . . . building, testing, discarding . . . while expenses piled up.

At last an answer came from the Ordnance Department. They were willing to watch a demonstration, but they would not promise to buy the gunlock.

"Why, those idiots!" John stormed. "Those . . ." When he was done exploding, he asked, "Now what?"

Mr. Braithwaite glanced toward the safe, where the final model of the gunlock was hidden. "We'll let it stay where it is, until the gentlemen come to their senses. Meantime—we have work on the boiler."

How much longer, John wondered, could they go on this way—spending money hand over fist, with no return?

One day they came into the office after a long session in the plant. A letter was propped on John's desk. He glanced at it, then sank in his chair with his head in his hands.

"John! What's wrong?"

"It's from my regiment."

"Your one-time regiment, you mean. You resigned months ago. I remember when we talked of how much leave you had, and—"

"But I didn't resign," John mumbled.

"*What!*"

"It just slipped my mind."

"Good heavens, boy! Then you're—"

"A deserter."

7

Night Gangs to the Rescue

"A deserter!" Mr. Braithwaite stared at John, appalled. "But they couldn't say that! They—"

"What else can they say?"

"But if you'd explain to them that . . . No, that's not the way to say it." Mr. Braithwaite walked the floor. He paused. "If you . . . No, that wouldn't help, either." He paced again. Once more an idea stopped him. "Suppose you tell them—"

"There's no excuse for what I've done!"

Mr. Braithwaite could not argue the point. "What will they do to you?"

"What does any regiment do to a deserter?"

"They wouldn't shoot you—not in peacetime."

"They'll dismiss me in disgrace. That's worse! I'd rather be shot than dismissed in disgrace! I'll shoot myself before—" He broke the seal and opened the letter. He scanned it, then jumped to his feet. "Read it!" he yelled. "Read it!"

Lieutenant Ericsson was now Captain John Ericsson of the Royal Chasseurs, by order of Oscar, Crown Prince of Sweden.

"Congratulations, John!"

"Captain Ericsson, to you, sir!" John grinned, and wheeled toward his drawing board. "What's more, I know how we'll get condensation in that boiler without shooting a jet of water—"

Mr. Braithwaite grabbed his arm. "Just a minute! What are you going to do about your regiment?"

"Resign, of course."

"Then write that resignation *now!* Before you forget again."

John laughed, sat at his desk, and wrote. "And some-day soon," he said, "I'll write to Prince Oscar, too. I'll tell him I've resigned from the Royal Chasseurs, but that I'll carry that title of captain the rest of my life. That I'll—"

"Write *that* letter, too. Before you forget *it!*"

John wrote it.

"And now," Mr. Braithwaite said, "I'm taking Captain Ericsson to supper to celebrate."

"But I—"

"That drawing board will wait until morning!" With

mock anger Mr. Braithwaite snarled, "You'll eat, if I have to spoon-feed you!"

"I put you to a lot of trouble, don't I?"

"You're worth it, John. You're quite an asset."

John thought of the cost of their experiments. "So far I've been nothing but a liability."

"The day will come when every one of these experiments will pay for itself."

"I hope so. We can't go on this way forever!"

"No," Mr. Braithwaite admitted, "we can't."

They had made the first tests on a new boiler when a letter came from Captain John Ross. Could Braithwaite and Ericsson furnish him a boiler of their latest and most improved design? He wanted to use it for experimental work for the navy.

John had never seen Mr. Braithwaite so excited. Generally he took everything, good luck and bad, very calmly.

"What luck! What superb luck, John! I thought it might be ten years before we could interest the navy!"

"Ross?" John asked. "Isn't he an Arctic explorer?"

"He went on one expedition, a few years ago. Wasn't too successful. I've heard he tried to get the Admiralty to send him out again, but they refused."

"His bad luck is our good luck," John said. "Steam navigation isn't ready for an expedition to the Arctic, but for experimental purposes for the navy—"

"We couldn't ask for a better chance than this!"

They built the boiler for Captain Ross. The ship to be used for his experiments was brought around to the Thames and put in dry dock for alterations. She was the *Victory*, a paddle-wheel steamer.

Mr. Braithwaite studied the paddle wheels. They were of a new design. "Captain Ross won't experiment long with those," he said. "That housing will block the flow of the water."

John shrugged. "After all, when you are experimenting, you don't consider complications. Sometimes you learn more by setting up a new situation than you do by following a beaten trail."

They installed the machinery in the *Victory*. Mr. Braithwaite shook his head again over the paddle wheels. "If those work, I'll eat them!" he declared.

They had completed installation on the *Victory* when a message came from Captain Ross. Could they see him that evening? They went.

What he had to tell them, the Captain said, must be held in confidence. "Gentlemen, I am sailing on a second expedition to the Arctic, in search of the Northwest Passage!"

"No!" John shouted. "That's the—"

Captain Ross smiled. "Surprised? You probably heard that the Admiralty turned me down. Mr. Felix Booth is financing the expedition."

"But why in the name of—" John began.

Mr. Braithwaite grabbed John's arm to silence him. He spoke quietly. "Captain Ross, why didn't you take us into your confidence?"

The whole thing had been kept secret, Captain Ross said. He had not wanted another expedition to steal the march on him.

Nothing betrayed Mr. Braithwaite's feelings but the way his fingers bit into John's arm. "Captain Ross, we worked in good faith, building and installing a marine boiler for experimental purposes. It has several innovations that will be a boon to steam navigation—we hope. We came here, ready to offer to consult with you, any time you returned to port; ready to make alterations, at our expense, if anything seemed to be giving trouble. Now we find you will be gone at least a year—"

"Longer," Captain Ross said.

"You'll be completely out of touch with us—beyond any help if trouble develops."

"I thought," Captain Ross snapped, "that I was ordering—and paying for—the most improved design in a marine boiler!"

John shook off Mr. Braithwaite's hand. "You asked for a boiler for experimental purposes! You got that! You—"

Mr. Braithwaite stopped John again. "When do you sail?"

"Before the end of May."

"Then we'll work on the machinery—at our own expense—night and day between now and then. We'll try to get rid of any experimental features that we had hoped to have tested."

A crew of their best men worked every day. A night gang took over, and continued the work, every night. John never left the ship.

On May 23 the *Victory* sailed. The partners went with her as far as Gravesend. They were having plenty of trouble with the ship. Her original tonnage had been increased by building her up. She was leaking. Moreover, she was riding too low in the water.

At Gravesend they left the *Victory*. Heartsick, John watched her churning sluggishly down the Thames.

The mood of the shop men did nothing to cheer him up. He heard Bill Sanger grumbling. "Hurry! Hurry! Hurry! Night gangs all the time! Before *that* one joined us, we never had this sort of business!"

Late in July a letter came from Liverpool. John recognized Mr. Wallace's handwriting. "Good! Maybe he's coming to London!"

A clipping fell out of the letter, dated the past April. "You probably saw this," Charles Wallace had written on it. The clipping announced a contest for designers of steam locomotives.

In October—five months from the date of the announcement—there would be a trial of locomotives at

Rainhill, near Liverpool. A prize of five hundred pounds would go to the best locomotive. It must not weigh over six tons. It must be able to draw a load of three times its weight at ten miles an hour.

John read the letter:

Can't you pay me a visit in October? We could watch this contest together. It should be very exciting. I hear that at least a dozen locomotives will be entered.

Of course, most people are jeering at the idea. They don't believe any locomotive can reach that impossible speed. One official said that if a steam locomotive did average ten miles an hour, he "would eat a breakfast of stewed engine wheels."

But George Stephenson thinks it can be done, and he is the man who ought to know. For several years he has been building locomotives to haul coal from the mines. He and his son, Robert, are building one for the contest—the Rocket. They'll doubtless win.

John gave the letter and clipping to Mr. Braithwaite. "Think we can do it?"

"Go to Rainhill?"

"Enter a locomotive."

"What!"

"Design it, build it, and have it ready to ship to Liverpool in seven weeks!"

70

"But, John, what do we know about steam locomotives?"

"The conditions of success. Just enough weight to give traction on the rails. Tremendous power for that weight. We must have a more efficient boiler than . . ." John's voice trailed off. His eyes narrowed. He wandered out of the office.

The plant saw nothing of him for a few days. Then one morning he breezed in, marched to his drawing board, and began to sketch. "It's going to mean night gangs again," he said. "*You'd* better tell the men."

Once more their men worked around the clock. This was the craziest one yet, they said. Utterly impossible. But they did it. They built the locomotive, christened it the *Novelty*, and shipped it in time for the trials.

Charles Wallace met John in Liverpool. "You got here in time! Good!"

"And so did the *Novelty*."

"How in heaven's name you did it, I don't know."

"I'm not sure I know, either," John said. "How many engines are entered?"

"Four."

"I thought more than a dozen were being built?"

"They were. Their designers could not get them ready in time. They are raising quite a fuss. Saying five months wasn't long enough. One said he would need at least a month after his locomotive was done—to season green

71

joints. I've heard of green wood, but not of green metal."

"Sometimes there are leaks in joints," John said. "The sediment in water will eventually stop them."

"So joints may be 'green' until they are dirty enough?"

"That's one way of putting it." John started to smile, then yawned.

Mr. Wallace spoke quickly. "You're worn out! Come along! You've got to get more rest before the trials."

John nodded. But that night he tossed and turned and could not sleep. He had been going at top speed too long to unwind quickly.

"We'll get an early start," Mr. Wallace said the next

morning. "They are expecting quite a crowd. Maybe a thousand or fifteen hundred. The officials have hired fifty men to keep the tracks cleared."

Rainhill was bedlam. Ten thousand people had come to watch the contest. The officials rushed three hundred special policemen into the breach.

They darted here and there, begging, "Please, ladies and gentlemen! Please! You must keep clear of the rails! The locomotives must have a chance!"

But the excited mob shoved and elbowed one another on and off the tracks and gazed at the locomotives.

The *Novelty* looked very small. Water tank and all, it

weighed only fifty-five hundred pounds—not half the weight limit.

Beside it, the Stephensons' *Rocket* was massive. With the separate tender that carried its water tank, it weighed eighty-three hundred pounds.

Neither of the other engines met the specifications, but the judges were allowing them to be run. The consensus seemed to be that the *Rocket* had the prize won before the race started.

John knew better. Tired as he was, he could smile as he listened to the frantic policemen. "Please, ladies and gentlemen!"

It was late before the contest could begin.

One of the judges addressed the crowd. There had been loose talk, he said, that the locomotives might go twelve, fifteen, or even twenty miles an hour. He wished to put a stop to such wild speculation. They had asked for a speed of ten miles an hour with a load. That was fast enough! Twenty miles an hour would be criminal folly!

The contest began. The *Rocket* made the first run. The judges announced the result: The Stephenson locomotive, with a load of more than twelve tons, had averaged ten miles an hour!

The crowd cheered.

The judges ordered the *Rocket* to make a second run without a load. The crowd watched, openmouthed.

Eighteen miles an hour this time! More cheers.

"I can beat that speed with a load," John whispered.

"You've done it?" Mr. Wallace asked.

"No. I had no chance to."

"Then how can you be sure?"

"Because I designed the *Novelty!*" John grinned. "You know, the *Rocket* is well named. Notice that rocking motion? The angle of the drive shafts. A little more speed, and the *Rocket* would rock the smokestack loose."

"Yes, that smokestack is rather . . ." Mr. Wallace stopped. He stared at the *Novelty*. "John! Your smokestack . . ."

"Seems rather short, doesn't it?"

"But how will you get draft to—"

"A special blower. The faster I go, the more draft I'll have."

An official approached the *Novelty*. "There is not time for you to make more than one run today, Captain Ericsson. You may make a run without a load."

The *Novelty* started. She quickly picked up speed— and more speed. She streaked down the track. She averaged thirty-two miles an hour.

The crowd looked on, dazed. So did officials, judges, reporters, and policemen. The other locomotive designers had the blankest faces of all.

The first day's trials were over. Reporters gathered

around the *Novelty,* talking so fast they tripped on one another's words:

"The nerve of you, daring to go that fast!"

"Of course, they'll never haul passenger cars at thirty miles an hour."

"Never! Even if the locomotives could do it, nobody would want to ride at that breakneck speed!"

"But, man alive, what a thing to see happen!"

"How could it ever get that speed? Nothing about it is big enough."

John let them talk. That night, for the first time in weeks, he slept so heavily that Mr. Wallace had to shake him awake in the morning.

At Rainhill, John noticed several men strolling by, scowling at the *Novelty,* and muttering to one another.

"What's the matter with them?" he asked.

"I think they have heavy wagers on the *Rocket,*" Mr. Wallace said. "Now, for the first time, they think there is competition."

"Competition?" John grinned. "This is annihilation!"

One of the directors came up and cleared his throat with a pompous "Hurrumph!" He said, "We'll not expect your little engine to haul the load that the *Rocket* can handle."

"The *Novelty* will meet the terms of the contest! Three times its weight at ten miles an hour! And more, too!" John said.

"More of which?" the director asked. "More weight, or more speed?"

"More of both!"

The workmen loaded the cars to eleven tons. The *Novelty* puffed. The cars creaked. They moved. They went faster. The *Novelty* averaged twenty-one miles an hour—with a load!

A sudden downpour scattered the crowd and flooded the tracks. The contest was called off until the next fair day. John did not care. The contest might not be over, but he had already won. He had given them double their speed, with more than the required load.

Two days later, an even bigger crowd swarmed to Rainhill. The frantic policemen raced up and down even faster. "Please, ladies and gentlemen!"

One of the judges made an announcement. They wished to test the durability of the locomotives. Each engine would make twenty round trips on the mile and a half of track. They signaled for the *Rocket*.

What with starting, stopping, switching—and keeping the track cleared—the *Rocket's* trial took all day. What a magnificent performance! An average of fifteen miles an hour with a load!

John cheered with the crowd. Let the *Rocket* have its day. Tomorrow it would go down to defeat.

The next day the *Novelty* ran. Two round trips—and beating the *Rocket* every foot of the way! The third round trip started. John heard the noise and knew instantly what it was. A leak in one of the green joints of the boiler.

He had lost. He might design and build the most revolutionary locomotive in the world in seven weeks. He might give the judges speed that had their jaws agape. But he could not season green joints that fast. Only time could do that.

The *Novelty* was withdrawn from the contest.

It did not take long to demonstrate the other two locomotives. Neither could meet the requirements.

The *Rocket* had won.

8

Fire!

There was a banquet in Liverpool to award the prize to the Stephensons, designers of the *Rocket*. Mr. George Stephenson made a gracious speech of acceptance. The locomotive, he said, was not the product of any one man. It was the product of a nation of engineers.

John smiled. He applauded. But the whole affair had a taste of ashes.

A middle-aged man introduced himself to John. He was Francis B. Ogden, he said, American consul to Liverpool. "I didn't get to talk to you at Rainhill. Your *Novelty* was magnificent."

"Thank you."

"I heard someone saying the boiler exploded. Idiots. Just a green joint, wasn't it?"

Puzzled, John answered. Yes, it was a green joint. Hadn't the man said he was a consul?

79

"How long have you been in England, Captain Ericsson?"

"Three years."

"Congratulations! You've made more of an impression on their engineering world in three years than I have in twelve!"

"But I understood you to say you are consul to—"

Mr. Ogden's quirky eyebrows cocked. He chuckled. "Americans are jacks-of-all-trades. Especially Yankees. I was a soldier first, an engineer second, and a diplomat third. You know, when President Jackson offered me this post, I took it because I wanted to see what they were doing with steam engines over here. Especially with steam navigation. So Liverpool suited me fine. Some of the best shipbuilders are here. And I'll tell you this, Captain Ericsson: Transatlantic steamers are coming! Have you ever been interested in marine engines?"

"We built a boiler 'for experimental work for the navy,'" John said. He added grimly, "At least, that was what we thought we were doing." He told of the work on the *Victory*.

"Must have been a bitter disappointment."

"We've had several of those." Somehow it was easy to talk to Mr. Ogden. John even told him about the flame engine. "You see, I started my career in England with a rousing failure!"

"That's how an inventor succeeds," Mr. Ogden said.

"One rousing failure after another. We have to break the trail. So we build and fail till we find the answer. That's why the fool public calls us 'impractical.' The idiots!"

John laughed. Earlier that evening he had not felt that he would ever laugh again, but now he did.

"Don't let the disappointment about the *Victory* stop you," Mr. Ogden said. "You keep thinking about steam navigation. Especially for the navy! Because the steam warship is coming!"

"If we can get rid of the paddle wheel," John said.

"Hmmm. . . ." Mr. Ogden studied, then nodded. "Captain Ericsson, when you find the answer to that, let me know! I'll help you with a patent in the United States, if you wish. I'll help you any way I can!"

John stared, bewildered, at the amazing man. What an offer from a perfect stranger! "Thank you, sir."

"No thanks needed. Young man, the world is going to hear more of you! You are a mechanical genius!"

With Mr. Ogden's card in his pocket, and Mr. Ogden's cheering words in his mind, John took the stagecoach for London.

"Where is the *Novelty?*" Mr. Braithwaite asked.

"On the way. I saw her loaded before I left Liverpool."

"Too heavy to throw?" Then he smiled. "John, don't let that affair upset you too much. Maybe the *Rocket*

won, but all England is talking about the *Novelty*
We'll work on locomotives. Experiment when we have
more time."

More experiments. More expenses. When would his
work begin to pay?

"Come along," Mr. Braithwaite said, "I'll take you
to supper."

The night was crisp, with a brisk wind. "Feels good,"
John said. "Let's walk."

They had just finished eating when they heard a
commotion in the street. They went outside. An excited
throng was hurrying toward a glare that lighted the sky.

"Fire!" Mr. Braithwaite said. "And what a ghastly
night for it. With this wind, half of London could burn."

A rowdy crew of firemen came racing down the
street, dragging their engine, knocking people out of
their way.

An elderly man careened against Mr. Braithwaite. "I
beg your pardon!" he gasped. "Sometimes I wonder
which is worse—the fires or the firemen!"

Another yelling crew passed, plunging recklessly
through the people.

"Walk with us," John said. The three went toward
the fire together. A two-story building was blazing,
with flames shooting out of the upper-story windows.

The fire brigades were pumping feverishly, but the
streams of water hissed and turned to steam without
affecting the flames. Other crews trained their hose on

nearby buildings, trying to put out all flying embers.

"They need bigger hose," John said. "Of course that would take more power to . . ."

He snapped back to the present when he realized Mr. Braithwaite had spoken to him. "I'm sorry. Did you say something?"

"Yes. About ten minutes ago. I said, 'Don't you think we'd better go back to the office?' "

"We were going to do something there?"

"Well . . . that's where your drawing board is."

When the plans for a steam fire engine were drawn up, John said, "With a six-horsepower engine, we can pump a hundred and fifty gallons a minute. And we can throw a stream of water a hundred feet high!"

"Our men will be mighty interested in this," Mr. Braithwaite said.

"So long as we don't ask for night gangs?"

"I believe they'd even be willing to work on night gangs for this."

Mr. Braithwaite talked to the men. He told them of the power the fire engine would have. "I don't have to tell you men how important this fire engine is. Now, we can work at it, along with our other jobs, and get it done—eventually. Or we can use night gangs and get it done as soon as possible. We're going to leave that decision to you men."

"Night gangs!" one yelled. Then he added, "But

make them as didn't work nights on the *Novelty* do this, eh?"

"That's for you men to decide," Mr. Braithwaite said. "Here's one suggestion. Maybe we should ask the single men to volunteer for the night gangs? Because they don't have families waiting for them at home?"

"Not fair!" one begged. "The married man already *has* his missus! Wot about us as ain't won our missus yet?"

Bill Sanger jeered. "Arrrr! Let the poor blokes as must bow to women worry about that! If I tells my Maria I'm busy, she says, 'Yes, Bill, dear!' meek as a lamb!" Bill swaggered across the floor and faced the men. "I say we have volunteers for the night gangs! Just men as *are* men! Come on! Step up! Who's goin' to work on Mr. Braithwaite's engine?"

Mr. Braithwaite's engine, John thought. They have never accepted me.

But they worked with a will on the engine. They bragged about it before it was half built. They named it the *Conqueror.*

When it was ready to test they took it out into the country, where they had a stream of water and a high tree. One man climbed the tree to hang a marker at the hundred-foot height.

They fired the boiler. It took twenty minutes to get up steam. Then they started the pump, and a jet of water burst from the hose, almost jerking it from the hands of the men. Higher and higher it shot, and hit the hundred-foot marker.

"Hurrah for the *Conqueror!*"

"You've done it, Mr. Braithwaite! You've done it!"

"*We've* done it," Mr. Braithwaite said. "Captain Ericsson and I—with the help of all of you."

His words were lost in their shouts.

I'm still just a foreigner to them, John thought. *Clever, maybe, but a foreigner.* But what did it matter who got the credit? He and Mr. Braithwaite knew how they worked together.

They went back to the plant.

"Now," Mr. Braithwaite said, "to figure the costs, so we can talk to the managers of the fire brigades."

"The cost of *this* one," John asked, "or of the future ones?"

Mr. Braithwaite only smiled. "I think we'll talk to Mr. Jennings first."

"You'll swear to this?" Mr. Jennings asked. "A hundred and fifty gallons a minute? To a height of a hundred feet?"

"We've done it."

"Mr. Braithwaite, you are going to have a problem on your hands!"

"A problem?"

"Steam fire engines, for London alone, would tax three plants the size of yours. And when London uses the steam fire engine, all England will!"

"I hope so," Mr. Braithwaite said. "Not just for the sake of our company. For the sake of our cities. A serious fire—"

"All fires are serious," Mr. Jennings said. "Especially if there's a wind. Four times London has been almost destroyed. The last time more than thirty-five thousand houses went up in flames."

He promised to bring a group to see the steam fire engine as soon as possible. He shook hands. He went. When he had gone, the partners shook hands with each other.

Before the managers came to see the *Conqueror*, there was a chance for a practical test—and a spectacular one.

The Argyll, a huge concert hall, was burning. The night was bitterly cold, with a high wind. When the *Conqueror* got to the fire, a dozen hand-pumped engines were already in operation. It was plain that the Argyll was beyond saving. The desperate fight would be to prevent the spread of the blaze.

Although the men knew it would take twenty minutes to get up steam, they chafed at the delay. Four men, waiting their turns on a hand pump, gathered around the steam fire engine.

"Wot you call this?"

Bill Sanger's bulldog jaw threatened them: "The *Conqueror!*"

"Of wot?"

"You'll see *wot!*"

"Gather round!" one jeered. "We're goin' to see somethin'—'e says."

Fists doubled, Bill started for his heckler.

"None of that," Mr. Braithwaite said. "The *Conqueror* will speak for itself."

And the *Conqueror* did speak, in a jet of water that shot to the top of the dome of the Argyll. The watching people gasped, then cheered.

The panting crews on the hand-pumped engines stepped up their strokes, but the streams from their hose were a trickle compared to the jet from the *Conqueror*.

Then, one after another, the hand pumps failed. The hose froze and burst. After two hours, only the *Conqueror* was working. The crowd that had come to watch the fire stayed to watch the new fire engine. John heard their murmurs of excitement and pleasure. Then he heard another sound—a sob.

He turned. A girl—quite a beautiful one, too—was watching the blazing dome of the Argyll, with tears running down her face.

He touched her shoulder. "Why are you crying? Can I do anything?"

"Oh . . . " She put her hand to her cheek. "I didn't

realize I was crying. But it's like seeing a friend die. All my life I've heard the loveliest concerts in the world here. And now—it's going. Even this new engine can't save it, can it?"

"No, but when we build a hundred—five hundred—and have them all over the city—so they can get to fires quickly—then we'll save other concert halls."

"You did this? You built the engine? Oh, thank you! And thank you for trying to save the Argyll! It was very kind of you!"

Bill Sanger was swaggering before the onlookers now, shouting, "There it is, ladies and gentlemen! There is the answer to all those little hand-pumped contraptions! The *Conqueror* can do the work of fifty men, and do it better!"

The people laughed, but there was a deep-throated growl from the men of the fire brigades. Six of them, shoulders hunched, heads lowered, fists cocked, were sneaking up on Bill from behind.

John leaped. He grabbed the first one, swung him up at arm's length, and hurled him against the others. They went down in a heap, picked themselves up, and retreated, snarling.

John turned to where the girl had been standing, but she was gone.

For five hours the *Conqueror* worked without a hitch, throwing its stream of water to the top of the

Argyll, and then on nearby buildings. At last the fire was out.

Bone-tired, sooty, but triumphant, they returned to the plant. Mr. Braithwaite offered the men of the fire crew a holiday.

"Arr!" Bill said. "Let them as can't lose a little sleep take the day off! Me, I say we've got to keep this other work movin'—so we'll be ready when the orders come in! For Captain Ericsson's engine!"

Mr. Braithwaite smiled. "Just as you say, Bill." He led the way to the office.

As John followed, he could hear Bill. "Just picked the one up, he did, and knocked the others down with him! And never even mussed his hair!"

Mr. Braithwaite chuckled, then grew sober. "John, those fire brigades are a rowdy lot."

"I think we can handle them."

"I'm wondering if their managers can?"

"What do you mean?"

"Let's see what their managers have to say about the steam fire engine."

"What can they say? Except that it's a godsend?"

Mr. Jennings came, flanked by two other managers. The steam engine was hardly practical, was it? Taking so long to get up steam. Just think of the headway a fire could make in twenty minutes.

"What about the headway a fire makes when your

hand pumps stop?" John roared. "Our engine worked three hours the other night after everything else was out of commission! And what hand pump can hurl a stream of water a hundred feet in the air?"

That was another thing, Mr. Jennings said. Really too much power. Rowdy men might do a lot of damage with such a powerful stream of water. Turn it on a crowd, or something of that sort.

The others nodded. They thanked Mr. Braithwaite for the demonstration. Very interesting. But—er—ah— they really could not approve the purchase of steam fire engines.

John stared, unbelieving, as the managers left. "You mean they'll actually turn it down, because they are afraid of their rowdies?"

Mr. Braithwaite said, "Exactly."

"They'll risk seeing half the city burned someday, because they don't have better fire-fighting equipment?"

"John, this has been the history of every mechanical improvement I know of. When a machine can do the work of fifty men, there is always a mob ready to destroy it. I haven't given up. I'll continue to send it to every fire, at no charge. Maybe—just maybe—public opinion will save the steam fire engine before some gang destroys it."

The next day Mr. Braithwaite got an anonymous letter. The day after, two more. They were all in the same vein. He had no business trying to put honest men out of work. If he sent that infernal machine out again, it would be wrecked.

They did send it out. They sent it to every fire they could reach. They hoped against hope that public opinion would force the fire brigades to accept it. Twice fire brigades spent more time fighting the *Conqueror* than fighting the fire. Mr. Braithwaite gave up in disgust. One more invention must wait for the day when people would accept it.

9

Ericsson vs. *The Admiralty*

The craze for railroads was sweeping the country. The partners turned again to work on steam locomotives. They built two—at a staggering cost. But they did not win a contract with a railroad company. Locomotives of the Stephenson design were sweeping the country, too.

One day, in 1833, John stopped working long enough to take stock. Seven years in England, and what did he have to show for them? Some small successes—quite a few, in fact. Everything from a pump to clear water from a mine, to a sounding device for ships. He had been taking out at least four patents a year. Or, rather, Englishmen had been taking them out for him.

A Mr. Carl Seidler had helped out several times. He never seemed to worry about whether or not a patent was going to pay off immediately. "Someday," he always said, "you will come into your own!"

To date, John thought grimly, Mr. Seidler's prediction

had not come true. Nothing had balanced the cost of their experiments.

The idea of a war steamer still nagged at him. How could one get rid of the paddle wheels? A screw propeller? But men had tried that long since, and had given up. Could he design one that would work?

Once more the long process began: Design, test, discard . . . design, test, discard . . .

One day Mr. Seidler dropped in. "Captain Ericsson, I find you have another staunch admirer in my house. My young sister-in-law, Amelia Byam. She collected every word about the steam fire engine. Then she read everything about the *Novelty*."

"A budding engineeress?" John asked.

"Oh, no!" Mr. Seidler laughed. "Nothing grim like that. Music is her love."

"That's better. I wouldn't wish the life of an engineer on anybody—let alone a girl."

He accepted Mr. Seidler's invitation to dinner, to meet his "staunch admirer." Amelia was late coming downstairs.

Mr. Seidler chuckled. "I'll warrant she's changed her dress five times."

Mrs. Seidler smiled. "Please, Carl, don't tease her!"

"Now, dear, a little teasing never—"

John was on his feet, walking toward the girl in the doorway. "I remember you! At the Argyll fire!"

Amelia blushed. Her dark eyes glowed. "I didn't

think you would remember. But I'll never forget that night."

"What became of you?" John asked. "I turned away just a moment, and then you were gone."

"I ran. I was scared to death! There were six of those men! I heard what happened later. I wished then I had stayed. I thought you were the greatest man in the world."

John bowed. "And I knew that night that you were going to grow up to be the most beautiful woman in the world."

Mr. Seidler clutched his head in mock horror. "Oh, dear, there will be no living with her!"

But Amelia did not pose, or flutter her eyelashes. She had other things on her mind. "If I were a general," she declared, "I'd line up all the people that turned down your fire engine. And I'd shoot them. Every last one!"

It was a gay evening. John could not remember when he had laughed so much. The next morning, he had been at his drawing board an hour when Mr. Braithwaite came in.

"What's that you're whistling?" Mr. Braithwaite asked.

"Hmmm? Was I whistling?"

"You always do, at the drawing board. But I've never heard that tune before." He hummed a strain.

"Oh . . . An old Swedish love song. My mother used to sing it. Odd. I haven't thought of it in years."

"Pleasant time at the Seidlers'?" Mr. Braithwaite asked.

"Delightful." John finished the sketch. "There—if we try that pitch on the propeller, I believe we've got it!"

"How was your 'staunch admirer'?"

"Who?"

"Amelia Byam."

"Oh . . . Lovely girl."

"How old?"

"I've no idea. Maybe sixteen or seventeen." And John went into the shop to see about making up this new design.

He made it in miniature, and put it in a little model boat. He floated the boat in a circular tank, and fed steam into it through a flexible hose. If this design was the answer . . .

It was not. He picked up the little boat, smashed it into a pile of scrap iron, and left the shop. The search began again: Design, test, discard . . .

In September, amazing news spread over England. Captain Ross, long given up for lost, had returned from the Arctic. Everybody cheered. They honored him with banquets. They awarded him a prize. They knighted him. The Northwest Passage? No, he had not found that. But to think of a leader surviving four years in the Arctic!

John and Mr. Braithwaite waited for some word from

Ross. There was nothing. They did hear of his answer to a reporter's question:

"The steam machinery of the *Victory?* It's in the bottom of the ocean! I have no comment now. I'll say what I have to say later!"

"What the devil did he mean?" John growled. "If he has something to say, why doesn't he come out with it?"

"Stick to the present, John," Mr. Braithwaite said. "We'll not gain anything by looking back. We may have a long road ahead of us before the screw propeller works. Don't waste time over Ross. We have no time to waste—or money."

"Things are bad?" John asked.

"You take care of the propeller, and I'll take care of the finances."

A year and a half later, in the spring of 1835, Sir John Ross published the story of his second expedition. Mr. Braithwaite brought a copy of the book to the office. There, for all the world to read, was "what he had to say—later." He blamed Braithwaite and Ericsson for the failure of his expedition.

John read, slammed down the book, and started to the door.

"Going somewhere?" Mr. Braithwaite asked.

"I'm going to challenge him to a duel!"

"Oh, no, you're not."

"Who'll stop me?" John yelled.

"I will. If I have to have you jailed for threatening a man's life."

"I'm not threatening his life! I'm challenging him—"

"I've heard of your marksmanship. If Captain Ericsson, of the Royal Chasseurs, challenges a man, that is a murder threat. I'll take care of this."

"How?"

"He accused us in print. I'll answer him in print. And you, my storming young viking, will stick to your drawing board!" It was an order, though he softened it with a smile.

John glared, but he turned back to his work.

One day soon after, when he was in a park "walking the cobwebs out of his head," he came face to face with Amelia Byam.

"Captain Ericsson!"

He swept off his hat and bowed. "My prediction came true. You did grow up to be the most beautiful woman."

Her eyes were stormy. "Have you seen that vile book of Ross's? If I were a better shot, I'd challenge him to a duel!"

John laughed. "And if I were a poorer shot, I would have challenged him."

"Are you still so busy?" she asked. "We've been so sorry that you have had to refuse our invitations to dinner."

Invitations? He had heard of no invitations. "Yes,

awfully busy," he told her. "But when I solve the problem of the screw propeller, I'll take a week off to celebrate! That's a promise!"

He went back to the office. Invitations? They would have been sent through Carl Seidler. Had he pretended to deliver them, and reported John's regrets? That must be the answer. Of course, Mr. Seidler knew how busy he had been . . .

John smiled. The next time I see him, I'll tell him I'm not quite *that* busy!

The next time he saw Mr. Seidler, though, he forgot about the lost invitations. He had just tested a new design of the screw propeller in a model boat two feet long. The boat had streaked around a cistern at three miles an hour!

Braithwaite and Ericsson raised the money—a hundred and fifty pounds—to take out a patent. Then John went to Liverpool to talk to Mr. Ogden.

"You've just now taken out your patent?" Mr. Ogden asked. "You haven't patented it during development?"

"Too much money," John said. "We couldn't throw away a hundred and fifty pounds every time we made some little change. But we've taken out a patent now."

"And six weeks ago a certain Mr. Smith took out a patent for a screw propeller."

John groaned. "What should I do now?"

"Get your propeller accepted as soon as possible, and

put it into practical use here in England. Meantime, my offer stands. I'll take out a patent for you in the United States."

Back in London, John sent a note to Amelia Byam. The time had come, he said, to celebrate. If there were some concert she would like especially to attend, he would get tickets for it.

When he opened his door to a knock the next evening, Carl Seidler stood there.

"Come in! Come in!" John chuckled. "You are the man who has been protecting me from interruptions, aren't you? I heard about the invitations I have been refusing."

Mr. Seidler's smile flicked and was gone. He sat down, stared at the floor a moment, then looked up. "John, I've come to talk to you, man to man. That fool girl thinks she's in love with you."

It took John a while to sort out his thoughts—and his feelings. At last he said, "She is no girl. She's a woman. And a very lovely one."

Mr. Seidler said nothing.

John's temper flared, and he struck with the first thing that came to his mind. "You don't think a long-time failure is a good matrimonial risk, do you?"

"John, if you had an income of a hundred thousand pounds, I wouldn't think you were a good match for Amelia."

"Thank you. Is that all?"

"Please, John, let's not quarrel. We've been friends too long. Amelia admires your genius. She would love everything about it—except that your work takes time. Time and solitude. She could never understand that."

"You're asking me not to see her?"

Mr. Seidler pulled a letter from his pocket. "Here is her answer to your note. She trusted me to deliver it."

"You're asking me not to see her?" John repeated.

"No, John. I'm just asking you to think, long and hard, before you do see her."

John was still thinking when dawn streaked the sky. He knew the truth now. He was in love.

He took Amelia to the concert. It was another gay evening. She thought of a dozen blood-curdling ends for all who didn't appreciate his genius. John wondered when he had laughed so much. Probably not since the last time he had been with her.

He did not ask for another engagement. He was going to be busy, he told her. He had just written an article, defending the screw propeller, for a scientific magazine.

"I'll probably be engaged in a running feud with all the engineering brains in England—especially the Admiralty."

She thought up some more fates for them—especially for the Lords of the Admiralty. He went home, laughing to himself.

Sometimes when he walked in the park, he met her.

After a time his walks became more regular.

After two months he told her about Bernadotte—of how his wife had left him alone with his son in Sweden for so many years.

"That was beastly!" she said.

"Sweden was strange to her; her husband was busy; she was lonely."

"That's no excuse!"

"If you were married to a man who was very busy, would you be lonely?"

"How could anybody be lonely in London? Dr. Johnson said something about that once—that a man who was bored in London was already *dead*. Something like that."

"But if your husband—if his work took him away from London?"

"That's a silly idea," she said. "Everything important happens in London. You would never . . ." She stopped. "I mean—that's why you came to London, isn't it? Because it's the place for a great engineer?"

"I guess you know what I'm trying to say, don't you? I love you. When I have one success—just one—to offer you, I'll ask you to marry me."

"I don't care whether you've succeeded or not!"

"But I do."

"And I suppose that settles it?" she flared. Then she smiled. "Yes, lord and master!" They walked on in silence. Then she said, "I wish I were Queen Isabella. I'd sell my jewels and get you *six* ships! And you could put screw propellers in all of them!"

"Bless you."

"I wonder how long before somebody will believe?"

"I wish I knew!" was all he could answer.

Then success came. Three canal companies ordered screw propellers. John thought of all the canal boats in England. Maybe the shipbuilders weren't convinced yet, but that would come. Meantime, he felt sure enough of his future to propose.

He and Amelia went to tell the Seidlers.

Carl was alone. "So the canal companies are accepting the propeller? And you hope that will lead to a contract for a screw-propeller ship?"

"Of course!" Amelia said.

"Then why don't you wait to get married, until John does have a screw propeller in a ship?"

Amelia blazed. "I have faith in John! Even if you don't!"

"Wait a minute, my little spitfire! It's not a matter of faith. I know that someday John *will* build a screw propeller for a ship. And he'll be an awfully busy man while he's doing it. What if you waked up in the morning to find him already at his drawing board? What if he ate breakfast without talking, and dinner with a pencil in his hand? And didn't come home to supper at all?"

"Oh, please!" John said. "I'm not that bad!"

"You're worse," Carl said flatly. "But—if you two are determined to get married—you'll have my blessing. And—when Amelia comes weeping home to sister, her room will be waiting."

"You're beastly!" Amelia said. "I'll show you how mistaken you are!"

"I wish I could hope that," was all Carl said.

They were married in October. The men in the plant surprised John with a gift.

Bill Sanger made a speech. "We—uh—just wanted to say—uh—good for you, Captain Ericsson! Honest, we don't know how you ever got a wife, as busy as you are. But we're glad you did. A man—uh—uh—well, when you need night gangs on the screw propeller, we'll be with you, Captain Ericsson!"

Mr. Braithwaite was smiling as they went back into the office. Then he sobered. "I hope they're right, about needing night gangs to handle the contracts."

He had not wanted to worry John with their finances, he said. But Braithwaite and Ericsson needed contracts —a lot of them. They had waited a long time for this success. Almost too long. They had been buying time —with borrowed money.

"We still haven't convinced the Admiralty," he went on, "but God bless the canal companies! Long may they reign!"

A month later, two canal companies went bankrupt. The railroads, the paper said, were taking away their business.

John read the news and walked to the office in a daze. If the canal companies were failing, what about Braithwaite and Ericsson? Mr. Braithwaite had not come in yet. John was almost glad. He had a feeling he did not want to hear what Mr. Braithwaite would have to say. He sat down and tried desperately to collect his thoughts, to make plans.

Someone knocked. It was Mr. Ogden. He had heard about the failure of the canal companies. "No interest yet from a shipowner," he asked, "in the screw propeller?"

"None," John admitted. "And there's no prospect of it. Not a man in the Admiralty believes in it. So what other shipowner is going to invest money in it?"

"What if you built a tug powerful enough to tow a ship? A screw-propeller tug? Couldn't you prove something that way?"

"If we could build the tug," John said.

"Get me an estimate of the cost," Mr. Ogden said, "and I'll raise the money to build her."

John did not mince matters when he talked to Amelia. With two canal companies failing, the tug was their last chance. And time was running out. "I'm going to be the sort of husband Carl talked about," he said. "Working before breakfast and after midnight. We've got to prove something with that tug before our creditors close in on us."

"Yes, John."

"You'll understand?"

She made a face. "I'll hate that beastly little tug every minute you're working on it, but I'll love it when it's done."

Sometimes in the morning, John looked up from his drawing board to find Amelia sipping coffee and watching him. He would pause for a moment. "Good morning, dear. Where did you go yesterday?"

"Places!"

"See anyone interesting?"

"People."

They would laugh together.

Once she studied his face anxiously. "Please, John, don't work too hard!"

"Not a chance of it," he promised. To himself he thought, I can't work harder than I'm working now.

He found he could work harder if he had to. The Patent Office in Washington burned. All patent holders must refile. In the midst of the pressure of work on the *Ogden*, he had to prepare complete drawings on the screw propeller for Washington.

The building of the tug got under way. John saw even less of Amelia. He often went out without waking her;

he often returned after midnight. He began to leave notes for her, to report on the progress of the *Ogden:*

"The Beastly Little Tug will be launched today." . . .

"We're installing the machinery in the B.L.T."

Several shipbuilders and marine engineers watched the installation of the *Ogden's* machinery. They agreed that she would never work. The propellers were too heavy. They would rip the stern right out of her.

John did not bother to answer. He gave orders to fire the boilers. "And now," he said, "we'll find something to tow!"

"After we get her machinery in adjustment?"

"She's ready now."

"But how can you be sure before—"

"Because I designed her!"

The propellers began to turn. Steadily, smoothly, the *Ogden* moved through the water. John took the tug alongside a sailing vessel, the *Chester,* and requested permission to tow her.

The captain gave him permission to *try* to tow his ship. But the *Chester* was one hundred and forty tons!

They lashed the *Ogden* alongside. Grinning sailors manned the shrouds of the *Chester,* shouting advice. Their taunts stopped amid-jeer, leaving their mouths open. The *Chester,* with all sails furled, moved at seven knots against the tide.

The next day John approached an American packet

ship, the *Toronto,* six hundred and forty tons, and asked permission to come aboard.

"What's that contraption?" the captain asked. "No masts, no sails, no paddle wheels. How do you get around?"

"A screw propeller. This is the ship of tomorrow," John said. "The most powerful vessel of her size in the world."

"That so?" The captain grinned. "Wouldn't have to be very powerful to be that, would she? I could stow six of her on my deck. What can I do for you?"

"Give me permission to tow the *Toronto.*"

"With that? Well . . . I'll throw you lines. But I'll have a boat ready, to rescue your crew."

John stayed aboard the *Toronto* and signaled his men.

Word of the attempt to tow the *Toronto* spread quickly through the shipping in the Thames. Everywhere men were shoving, scrambling, and climbing to watch the fiasco. A vessel of fifteen tons tow a ship of six hundred and thirty tons? Forty-two times her tonnage? Ericsson was a madman!

They were still saying it could not be done when the *Toronto* began to move. She moved, against the tide, at four and a half knots.

Awestricken whispers from the sailors on the *Toronto*:

"It's spooky!"

"It ain't natural!"

"It's a devil! A flying devil!"

"That ought to be its name! The *Flying Devil!*"

John had a feeling the name would stick. The tug might carry *Francis B. Ogden* on her transom, but she would be the *Flying Devil* to the men on the Thames.

When news of this feat reached the Admiralty, even those men would listen!

The Admiralty seemed deaf to word of the *Flying Devil*. John wrote, asking permission to demonstrate the tug. The Admiralty replied. They would make no commitments or promises, they said. It would be wholly at his risk and expense that he would demonstrate the tug. The Lords of the Admiralty were scheduled to go from Somerset House to the Seward Iron Works, to inspect the progress of steam machinery there. Captain Ericsson might demonstrate his tug on that occasion.

John laughed as he read. What luck! He could not have asked for a better chance! They would see the contrast between those clumsy paddle wheels and the unseen power of the *Ogden!*

The *Ogden* steamed to Somerset House. They lashed her alongside the Royal Barge. John went aboard the barge. He knew the men of the Admiralty would bombard him with questions. He was ready. He spread the drawings of the machinery of the *Ogden* on a table.

They got under way. They moved at a steady ten knots.

"These drawings, Your Lordships," John said, "will explain the motive power of the *Ogden.*" He stood by the table, waiting for their questions.

They had none. They glanced at the table, then strolled away. They gathered in huddles. They talked together.

The barge reached the Seward Iron Works. The Lords of the Admiralty went ashore. They inspected the great paddle wheels. They returned.

Surely now they would question him!

But they did not. The *Ogden* towed them back to Somerset House. They thanked John for showing them his interesting experiment. They feared he had put himself to too much trouble and expense.

"Nothing, Your Lordships, is too much trouble or expense when it points the way to the steam warship of tomorrow!"

They did not answer that. Captain Beaufort promised a report in the near future. John gathered up his drawings and boarded the *Ogden*. They cast off. They steamed away.

His crew were eager. What had the gentlemen said? "Very little," John told them. "I think they were too amazed. Captain Beaufort said I'd get a written report!"

He could not fool Mr. Braithwaite with cheerful words. He did say, "When they've had time to think it over . . . As you said once, these things take time."

Mr. Braithwaite did not answer. John knew they were thinking the same thing. Braithwaite and Ericsson did not have time!

Captain Beaufort was a man of his word. The letter came quickly. Their Lordships, the captain regretted to state, had been quite disappointed in the demonstration.

"What the devil?" John said. "Why disappointed? What other vessel in the world, the size of the *Ogden*, could have towed that barge at ten knots?"

Mr. Braithwaite got up heavily. "I'll see if the banks will give us a little more time. I'll say that the Lords of the Admiralty are considering the screw propeller. It won't be an untruth. Surely they are talking about it!"

Yes, they were talking about it. All London heard of a dinner conversation on the subject. One dignitary of the Admiralty had expressed himself. The whole idea was preposterous. Even if screw propellers could move a ship, the scheme was quite useless. With power applied to the stern, they would never be able to steer a screw-propeller ship. It would never take the place of the paddle-wheel steamer.

"That's done it, John," Mr. Braithwaite said. "We're bankrupt."

10

Stranded Again

John did not know how long he had been walking, or where, when he found himself at the wharf looking at the *Flying Devil.* Thank heaven, the tug belonged to Mr. Ogden. It would not be lost with everything else in their bankruptcy.

He stared at the paddle-wheel steamers in the Thames, then back at the tug. Not a vessel there could match the power of the *Ogden,* ton for ton. But the man who had designed and built her was ruined.

He remembered his father, one long-ago morning. *"I have lost everything."*

Mother had said, *"Not everything, dear. We have our faith in tomorrow."*

I wonder, John thought, if I have any faith in tomorrow?

And Amelia—would she still have faith? Or would

she wish she had listened to Carl Seidler's advice? Would she weep and storm at him? He could not blame her if she did.

Amelia did storm—but not at John. "That Admiralty! I'd like to string them up by the thumbs! Every last man of them!"

She did not weep even when their belongings were sold. "We'll have better things than those someday!" she declared.

She went home to live with the Seidlers until John could get on his feet again.

Carl Seidler was full of sympathy. "I've been trying to find a position for you, John, but—"

"I've got a job," John said. "Some construction, where they are building a railroad. You know, I was a leveler once—when I was thirteen. I've made a lot of progress, haven't I?" Then he fought down his bitterness to say, "I'm glad Amelia can be here with you for a while."

Amelia's smile was a little shaky, but she did smile. "It won't be for long, John! I just know that! Something will turn up!"

John did not say what he was thinking. He smiled, too, and kissed her good-by.

On the new job his days were busy enough to keep him from looking back. But at night his failures haunted him. One morning he got up, still weary from a sleepless night, to find Mr. Ogden waiting to see him.

"Good news, John! At last there is a navy man who's interested in the *Flying Devil!*"

"I don't believe it," John said. "No navy man in England would—"

"He's not English. He's American."

Lieutenant Robert F. Stockton, Mr. Ogden said, was a man who had everything—family, breeding, money—and brains. He had entered college at thirteen. He had won his lieutenancy in the War of 1812. He had seen action everywhere that the American Navy had carried the Stars and Stripes.

"He's a hothead." Mr. Ogden smiled. "His nickname is 'Fighting Bob.' Got into an argument with some British in the Mediterranean once. Challenged the captains of a whole outfit. Offered to take them all on, one at a time."

"Good for Lieutenant Stockton," John said. "I'm going to like that man!"

Lieutenant Stockton lived up to Mr. Ogden's description. He was a handsome, dashing fellow, young-looking for his forty-two years. John did like him on sight.

He liked him even better when they boarded the *Flying Devil.* Here, for the first time, was a navy man who wanted to know all about the tug. Stockton studied the drawings. He asked questions. He listened.

They steamed up the Thames against the tide.

"This is magnificent!" Stockton said.

"The experts in England don't agree with you," John told him.

"Bah! I don't care what the experts say! One hour on this tug is all I need to convince me! This has given the lie to all the experts in the world! So—" he flashed a smile—"let's get down to business!"

The lieutenant, like Mr. Ogden, seemed to be a jack-of-all-trades. Not only was he an outstanding navy man, but he was also a financier, interested in various projects. Just now he was promoting the building of a canal in the United States. He wanted a tug for use on that canal.

"Something bigger than the *Ogden*," he said. "Let's say about thirty tons. Can you draw up rough specifications and give me an estimate on her before I leave England?"

John only nodded. He was beyond speech. For two years he had tried to make the British Admiralty believe in a screw propeller. Now, in two hours, he had sold the idea to an American naval man! Of course, he was not building a vessel for the navy. But—if a naval man believed—who knew what it might lead to?

He promised to have the rough specifications ready before the lieutenant left England. Well before the promised date, he gave Mr. Stockton not rough specifications, but the finished drawings, down to the last rivet, for an iron-hulled, screw-propeller tug to be called the *Robert F. Stockton*.

"The finished drawings!" Mr. Stockton whistled. "Mr. Ogden was right about you! You are amazing!"

"I've been a draftsman for more than twenty years," John said. He spread the drawings for the engine. "Now, here we'll have something new. I've designed an engine with enough speed to give direct action to the propeller. Much more efficient. We get rid of excess weight of extra gears and shafts."

"Direct action to the propeller?" Mr. Stockton studied the drawings. "It sounds impossible, but I believe you've done it! Though how you ever dreamed that it could be done—"

"I was thinking of a war steamer," John said. "She must be stripped of every possible pound of excess weight. So the direct-acting engine is a big move in the right direction."

After a thoughtful silence, Mr. Stockton nodded. He signed the contract for the tug and made a down payment. "You'll build her in Liverpool," he asked, "and arrange to ship her to America?"

"We can send her to America under sail," John said.

Mr. Stockton's eyebrows went up. "You mean you can build a tug, for shallow-water duty, that can sail across the Atlantic?"

"The vessel that's built to those specifications will be seaworthy."

"Captain Ericsson, you are the man I have been looking for! I have a feeling that this is only the beginning of our work together!"

Again John found it hard to speak. Would the day come when he would build a war steamer for the United States? He shook hands and hurried off to tell Amelia the good news about the new tug he was to build.

She had not wept at failure, but she did weep now over the good news. "It's been so awful without you, John! How soon can we be together again?"

"As soon as I can find a place for us in Liverpool," he promised.

Carl Seidler spoke quietly. "Amelia, if you really want to help John now, let him work on that boat without anything else on his mind."

"But, Carl—" she began.

"He's fighting for his life, Amelia. His professional life. A man doesn't carry a household into battle. Give him a chance."

Once more John told her good-by.

After a few days in Liverpool, he realized that Carl had been right. He had no time for anything but his work. He was superintending the building of the hull in one place, and the machinery in another. He found himself spending more and more time with the shipbuilders. There was so much that he could learn! Often at night he spent hours at his drawing board, sketching all he had thought about that day.

Quite a few builders of wooden ships came around to

shake their heads over the iron hull for the *Stockton*. She would never float, they said. She would sink like a stone.

The day came to launch the hull. Quite a crowd gathered to witness the disaster. John took a can of paint and drew a horizontal line on the starboard side of the hull. That, he said, would be the water line when she was launched.

"Plus or minus how much?" a man asked.

"Plus or minus nothing," John said. "That is the water line."

"You are the most conceited one man I've ever met."

John grinned. "If a man can't compute the displacement of an iron hull, he has no business calling himself a marine engineer!"

The *Stockton* slid down the ways. Silence. A cheer when she did not sink. Another silence, when she settled exactly to the water line that John had marked.

He got into a boat, went alongside the tug, and painted a second line above the first. "And that," he said, "will be her water line when I've installed her machinery."

Nobody had anything to say.

They did have plenty to say, though, when they heard that the *Stockton* would sail to America:

"He's crazy!"

"That Ericsson is mad!"

"He ought to be hanged if he sends men to sea in that tug!"

"Not much chance of that, is there?" one man asked,

with a twisted smile. "Who would be fool enough to take that tug off soundings?"

A weather-beaten old captain spoke up. "I would. That Ericsson—well, when a man can calculate his displacement that exactly—I'd take any vessel he built anywhere he said it would go!"

Robert F. Stockton—he was Captain Stockton now—returned to England. He was delighted with the tug. He watched as they fitted her with masts and sails for the crossing. He listened, unconcerned, to the croakers. Another American, Captain Crane, seemed unconcerned, too. He was ready to sail the *Stockton* to America.

On April 13—evidently Captain Crane was not super-stitious—the tug sailed. A crowd watched in silence.

At last one man spoke. "Wonder what'll happen to her?"

"That's what we'll never know," another said. "What happened, or where."

A knot twisted in John's stomach. How long would they have to wait for word of the *Stockton?* Had he been an arrogant fool to send the tug to sea? No, confound it, she was seaworthy! But, he reminded himself, even the most seaworthy ships were sometimes lost at sea. I wish, he thought, that for the next two months I could be so busy that I'd fall asleep at my work!

Captain Stockton called John into conference with him and Mr. Ogden. "Captain Ericsson, I've something to say in strictest confidence."

John nodded.

"I mean," Captain Stockton insisted, "this must go no further!"

John flared. "When a man tells me something in con-fidence, that's taken for granted!"

Mr. Ogden intervened. "Come, come, gentlemen! You'll both do better if you hold your tempers!"

They laughed.

"The Congress of the United States," Captain Stockton said, "has just authorized the building of three steam war-ships. And I intend to see that one of them is a screw-propeller vessel! Captain Ericsson, have you any ideas on the subject of a war steamer?"

"I have complete ideas."

"What assistance would you need to draw up plans for a war steamer of two thousand tons?"

"None."

"I mean the complete plans—engines, propeller, hull, bow, stern, all compartments—everything."

"That's what I mean, too," John said. "The complete ship—and her armament, too."

"Armament?"

"I served seven years in the Swedish Army," John said. "I have been familiar with big guns since eighteen-twenty."

"You have the most amazing assortment of information . . . Anything else, Captain Ericsson?"

"Yes." John leaned forward and lowered his voice. "Captain Stockton, I am going to tell you something in strictest confidence."

"Yes?"

"I mean—it must go no further."

Captain Stockton flushed. "When a man—" Then he laughed. "Go on, Captain Ericsson."

John sketched the plan of his automatic gunlock. "I designed that in 'twenty-six. We offered to demonstrate it to the Ordnance Department, on condition they would buy it if it lived up to our guarantee. They would not agree. I'm ready now to put that on a gun of my own design. I'm ready to build the gun, too."

"Amazing!" Captain Stockton said again.

Then he talked of the screw-propeller war steamer. If Captain Ericsson could furnish him with the plans, he would present them, personally, to the United States Navy. But the sooner he could have those plans, the better. They must be in Washington before the navy had spent all its funds for other vessels. Of course, it would probably be impossible to have the plans within six months . . .

It did not sound impossible to John. Twenty-odd years ago, hadn't he made his surveying maps so fast that he had been an embarrassment to his commanding officer?

"You'll have them!" he promised, and he went to London for a brief visit with Amelia.

She rebelled at the thought of another separation. Why couldn't John do this work in London?

"I need to be in Liverpool," he said. "I've friends there who can teach me a lot."

She scoffed at that. What was there left for him to learn?

"I'll never stop learning," he said. "The engineering world is changing so fast that I'll be running all my life to keep up with it. Sometimes I think that, as soon as anything works, it's out of date. Every time some old fogy says 'It'll never work,' I know that what he's talking about will work—someday. So I must be in Liverpool now."

She couldn't imagine anybody wanting to be that far from London. But, if he must go to Liverpool, she was going, too!

John found a flat for them, and his dawn-to-midnight work began. He was glad to have her with him, even though sometimes he said "Yes, dear," without knowing what he was "Yes, dearing" about.

At first Amelia was patient. After three weeks she flared up and said where she would like to send Captain Stockton, his ship, and the whole United States Navy!

John grinned. "Let's save that place for the British Admiralty, dear. It's the United States Navy that is going to give me my chance."

"What will happen?"

"When a ship, designed by one man, outclasses every other warship in the world—what do you think?"

Then he kissed her, said he might be a little late that evening, and went off to the foundry to see how the men were coming along with his wrought-iron gun.

There was not much he could do there. He returned to the flat in two hours—and found Amelia sobbing.

"Darling! What's happened?"

She tried to pull herself together. "Nothing. I—I—oh, John, it's so lonesome here!"

He thought back over the last three weeks. He

thought ahead to the weeks to come. "I was selfish to bring you here. You'll be better off back in London until these plans are done."

"But what about you?"

"I'll work like the devil," he said. "That's what a man does when he's lonesome."

"Carl will laugh at me, won't he?"

"Maybe."

"You'll write every day?"

"Of course!" he promised.

At first he did try to write every day. But what was there to tell her? "I enjoyed your letter. I love you." Then he wrote every week. Once he forgot, and did not write for ten days. He jotted notes on his calendar to remind himself.

One day he wrote a whole paragraph, telling her about his wrought-iron gun. It was ready for testing. He'd write all about it in his next letter.

They took the gun to a firing range to test it. They tried it first with fifteen, and then thirty pounds of powder.

"Uh-oh," a man said. "It cracked on that last firing, Captain Ericsson. We'll have to make a heavier gun."

"No," John said. "No excess weight we can possibly avoid. There has to be some other way to strengthen it."

"How?"

"I don't know—yet," John said. "I just know the conditions of success; the gun must have strength in both directions. I'll let you know when I find the answer."

After a few days he returned to the foundry. He made iron rings, just a fraction too small to slide onto the gun. He heated them white hot, and drove them onto the barrel. When they cooled, they were so tight that they looked as though they were part of the gun. He made a second set of rings, just a fraction too tight to fit over the first bands. He heated them and drove them on. When they had cooled, they were so tight that the two sets of bands looked like one.

They tested the gun again with fifteen pounds of powder—with thirty—with thirty-five. No cracks this time! Success! His war steamer would be armed with guns that could sink any ship in the world!

John returned from the firing range to find Mr. Ogden waiting for him.

"Did you hear about the *Stockton?*" Mr. Ogden asked.

John's heart lurched. "No."

"She made it! She's in New York!"

John slumped into a chair. Till that moment he had not admitted to himself how anxious he had been for word of the little vessel. Now it had come, and he went limp.

"She's the talk of New York!" Mr. Ogden said. "People are swarming to see her. Too bad you're not there. You'd be the man of the hour."

John laughed and jumped up. "What's a tug? Wait till they see the war steamer!" He celebrated the good news of the *Stockton* by working all night on his drawings.

Before the date he had promised them, he sent the completed plans to Captain Stockton.

Mr. Ogden took John to dinner that night to celebrate. "You should be relieved," he remarked, "but you're not, are you?"

"No," John admitted. "I feel lost. Of course, my job with the railroad is waiting for me . . ."

"John, you should go to America."

"What!"

"It's the land of tomorrow," Mr. Ogden said. "And you, John Ericsson, are a man of tomorrow."

"But I haven't the money to—"

"I can lend you money. After all, I have an interest in your going. An interest in my share in your patent for the screw propeller. I think if you were in America it might help protect your interest in it."

"I don't understand? My patent was accepted by the United States Patent Office. So long as I build propellers on that design—"

"You remember that you filed in 'thirty-five? And the Patent Office burned?"

"Yes, I remember the nuisance of refiling."

"Every inventor with any idea for a screw propeller is refiling. And there is no record of what their first sub·

mission was like. If they chose to introduce improvements—well, there could be some battles over the different patents. So the sooner you get your propeller introduced, the better. They'll soon be building your war steamer. You'll be known all over America. Strike while the iron is hot! While you are the man of the hour!"

In November John said good-by once more to Amelia. "It won't be for long, dear," he promised. "Just to get things started over there."

"You're sure it won't be long?"

"If I decide to stay longer than I think I shall, I'll send for you. You can come over and watch me be the 'man of the hour.'" He smiled. "And when the war steamer is done, we'll tour the country, and you can take the bows. How's that?"

With a model of his automatic gunlock safe in his luggage, and his wrought-iron gun stowed in the hold of the ship, John sailed for America.

Mr. Ogden came to see him off.

"I don't look forward to the crossing," John admitted.

"After the first few days you'll be all right," Mr. Ogden said.

But it was a stormy crossing. The last day out John wrote to Mr. Ogden:

*Just now, I don't feel like the "man of the hour."
I feel like the remains of a hard fight—that I lost.*

128

I'll add a note to this after I land. I'm sure I'll be feeling more cheerful then.

The note that he added was not more cheerful. He had found New York a city of gloom. The whole country was in the grip of a depression—banks failing—businesses going bankrupt—men in bread lines.

Captain Stockton had not been able to persuade the navy to build a screw-propeller war steamer.

The weather was beastly.

And—John could have added, but did not—another chill was biting deeper than the winter wind. Once more, in debt to a friend, he was stranded in an alien world, without prospects.

11

The Princeton

After a brief time of panic, John began to plan. His war steamer was only a dream, but his screw-propeller tug, the *Stockton*, was a fact. If he could get other contracts for tugs and lake steamers . . .

He wrote to Amelia:

It's going to be a little longer than I thought. As soon as I am on my feet, I'll send for you.

I'm living at the Astor House. I'm sure you'll enjoy it.

I've not time for more now. I'm taking my wrought-iron gun to a foundry. I'll leave it there, until plans for the war steamer are under way. Then I'll have them build the mate for this gun. Two guns like this will deliver a broadside that will sink anything afloat.

More later, dear. I'm off to the Phoenix Foundry.

Mr. Cunningham, of the Phoenix Foundry, said, "I'd like for young Harry Delameter to talk with you, Captain Ericsson. I'll be turning over more and more of my work to him. As soon," he added wryly, "as I can convince some people that a man doesn't have to be gray-headed to know his business!"

"How old is young Delameter?" John asked.

"Only nineteen, but he's—"

"Good!" John said. "At nineteen he won't be stuck fast in the past. Let's see him."

Harry Delameter was a sturdy young chap, fresh-faced, with level eyes. The look in his eyes said he was waiting for the usual objections to his youth. But John told of his days on the canal. Harry relaxed. At last he even smiled.

"Do you have time to take me through the foundry?" John asked.

Harry did. John asked dozens of questions.

Presently Harry turned to him with a broad grin. "Am I passing the test, Captain Ericsson?"

John's laughter boomed. "Harry Delameter, you're all right! We're going to get along fine!"

An old man left his bench and came to shake hands with John. "You're all right, too, Captain Ericsson. We're *all* going to get along fine!"

John was smiling when he left the foundry. Odd, how at home he felt in just two hours.

In the weeks that followed he grew to feel at home with the canal men and the shipbuilders. Soon he wrote to Mr. Ogden:

> *I think our claim to the patent is settled. Within a year or two my screw propeller will be on every lake and river in this land.*
>
> *And what a land it is! What a contrast to Europe! America is not chopped into many little countries, with soldiers standing guard on each border. Here, thousands of miles of inland waterways reach on and on, under one flag. It is the land of tomorrow.*
>
> *I'll never get used to the manners of these Americans. Especially at the table. They wolf down their food like starving savages. Fifteen minutes from the time they sit down at the table, they are up again, chewing the last bite.*
>
> *But I like them and I like the way they work!*

He did not try to explain to Amelia how he felt about the vastness of America. She would understand when she saw it. He sent her passage money to join him.

> *This is the happiest day of my life, dear. But a happier one will be the day I meet your ship!*

The morning her ship was to arrive, John leaped up from his drawing board, appalled. Where had the time gone? He was going to be late! He dashed out to the street, hailed a hack, and sat on the edge of the seat all the way.

Luckily the ship was late in docking. He was there in time.

Amelia was no better sailor than he was. She was almost too sick to stand. "I'll be all right," she whispered, "just as soon as things stop *moving.*" She looked at him with a little smile. "Poor darling, you've had a beastly long wait, haven't you? I could just see you, walking up and down, scowling!"

He didn't deny it. His stomach still felt hollow from the shock of thinking he would not be there to meet her. He must never let that happen again, he told himself. He must never get so wrapped up in his work that he forgot the time.

But he did. Again and again they arrived late for dinners, parties, or concerts.

"There is one thing I like about coming in late," he whispered one night. "I love to watch everyone looking at you."

There were concerts they missed when he forgot completely. There were other affairs they missed when he was called out of town.

At first Amelia was patient. She did say once, "I'll be so glad when we can go *home!*"

This is my home! John thought it, but he did not say it. Someday she would get used to America.

133

By the summer of 1841, his screw propellers were known all over America. But his plan for the war steamer was still gathering dust in the files of the United States Navy.

Then a letter arrived from Captain Stockton.

John read one sentence and said, "Amelia! At last they are going to build my war steamer!"

She groaned. "Oh, no! Is it going to be like that awful time in Liverpool?"

"Of course not, dear. My work is done. All I'll have to do now is to take the bows. And you'll take them with me!" He finished reading the letter.

There was the matter of cost to be considered, Captain Stockton wrote. The navy must know what Captain Ericsson intended to charge for the use of his patents. Perhaps, since this was the first trial on so large a scale, Captain Ericsson would be willing to wait for payment? Then, if the steamer proved successful, he would be willing to trust to the recommendation of Captain Stockton as to the amount of payment for the patents?

If it proved successful? John smiled as he read that. Yes, he wrote in answer, the matter of payment for the patent rights could wait until the ship had proved herself. And he would be satisfied with what Captain Stockton would recommend in payment.

"I wish they were building her in Brooklyn instead of in Philadelphia," he told Amelia.

"I don't! You already spend half your time in your

office and the other half at the Phoenix Foundry. If they were building that ship in Brooklyn, you'd spend *another* half of your life there."

He laughed. "You can't have three halves to one whole."

"Maybe not," she said, "but if anybody ever does figure out how to do it, you'll be the man!"

John laughed again, and sent his answer to Captain Stockton. Weeks passed. Restlessly, he wondered what was happening. If only he had an excuse to go to Philadelphia . . .

In October there was a hasty summons. Could Captain Ericsson meet Captain Stockton at his home in Princeton the following Tuesday?

"Why does he bother you?" Amelia asked. "I thought your work was done."

John did not admit how eager he was to go to Princeton. He found Captain Stockton full of enthusiasm. At last, the navy was going to build his ship! They would christen her the *Princeton,* after Captain Stockton's hometown.

"What a fight I've had to put it over!" he said. "But I've won! I'll build the first screw-propeller war steamer in the world! So we've got work to do!"

"I did my work in the summer of 'thirty-nine," John said. "The plans are complete."

There was a slight hitch, Captain Stockton said. The navy would not approve a two-thousand-ton war steamer. But they would approve one of six hundred tons. Could Captain Ericsson draw up general, over-all plans for a steamer of that size?

In a week John was back in Princeton with the plans. "There you are," he said. "With these to follow, your naval architects can work out detailed plans from the original drawings."

He hurried back to New York and picked up the work he had neglected. The matter of the *Princeton*, he told Amelia, was all taken care of.

"Thank goodness!" she said.

But more requests came from Captain Stockton. He needed detailed plans for this . . . for that . . . for the other thing. After two months John realized he was going to spend full time on the *Princeton*, and for a long time to come.

What of his home life? The answer, he decided, was to leave the hotel and get a house big enough to have his office at home. Then Amelia would not have to be alone so much.

He found a house on Franklin Street. Rather expensive—but he had to give Amelia a better life. She could not sit alone in a hotel all day while he was in his office.

Once more he was at his drawing board before breakfast. Once more he was saying, "Yes, dear," without hearing what he was answering.

One night Amelia interrupted his work by spreading her hands between him and his drawing.

"What's the matter?" he asked.

"I thought maybe you could stop long enough to talk it over," she said.

"Talk over what?"

"What you said, 'Yes, dear,' to a while ago. Or did you hear what I said?"

"Of course I heard you. I've forgotten for the moment, but—"

She spoke very quietly—so quietly that the room seemed to grow still with her. "I said, John, that I am going home to England."

"Amelia!"

"And you said, 'Yes, dear, of course.' "

"But—but—you can't do that! You—"

"Why not? I have no life here."

"But can't you realize how important this ship is to both of us? When it's done—"

"How long before it will be done? A month? Two months? Six months? I want the truth."

"Please, dear, can't you think about what it's going to mean when—"

"How much longer?"

Perhaps he had been wrong not tell her the truth in the first place. "Another year, at least," he said. "I have all these drawings to do. And they are going to need me as consulting engineer on the job, too."

"And then?" she asked.

"Success! And I'll rest on my laurels!"

"I can't imagine you 'resting' on anything," she said wryly.

"But I can! I can rest on success! You'll see! We'll take the trip we've never had! We'll see the world! We'll—"

"But—for at least another year—things are going on just this way?"

"Dear, doesn't it mean anything to you—that your husband is the one man in the world who can design every detail of a war steamer, from keel to top hamper? Engines, propellers, guns? When they mount my wrought-iron guns on her, and use my self-acting gun-lock—"

"You didn't answer my question," she said. "Or—come to think of it—I guess you did. That is the answer, isn't it? Things are going on just this way."

"But when the *Princeton* proves herself, and when all the world salutes the screw propeller—"

"Even England?" she asked.

He smiled. "Even England! When the Admiralty hears about the *Princeton*—"

"Then," she said quietly, "you may come home to England in triumph. I'll be waiting for you."

"You don't mean that! You're just—"

"Yes, I do. I'm going home, where I'll have something to do. I'm no help to you. I'm just an interruption—something in the way."

"You know how I'd miss you if—"

"I doubt it. You never know when I'm in the room now. I don't know why you'd notice that I was out of the room."

"I—I'm going to leave you to think this over," John said. He picked up his hat.

"*You* think," she said. "I've done my thinking. I've had lots of time."

This was once John could not "walk the cobwebs out of his head." Presently he found himself in front of a theater. How many times had he intended to take Amelia? He bought two tickets, fifth row center, and hurried home.

A letter from Captain Stockton was waiting. Some croakers were doubting the stability of the *Princeton.* Would Captain Ericsson please explain how he had arrived at the figures on displacement, metacenter, center of gravity, center of flotation . . .

It was midnight when John remembered the tickets. He sat a long time, snapping them with his thumb.

The next morning he left a note for Amelia: Stop me for breakfast, even if you have to hit me over the head!

He almost jumped out of his chair when she slapped him. "What the devil?"

"Following orders," she said. Her lovely eyes sparkled with mischief. "I spoke to you three times. You said, 'Yes, dear, I'm coming.'"

He laid down his pen, got up, and put his arms around

her. "Remember that day we talked about Bernadotte and his wife?"

She nodded. "I have more sympathy for her now."

"I do, too. You are right, dear. This isn't much of a life for you. Not until the *Princeton* is done. I'll see about your passage today. But when you get to England, will you tell Carl Seidler one thing for me? Tell him, if he laughs at you, I'll challenge him to a duel!"

"Oh, John, you are such a dear man—*when you're conscious!*"

The day Amelia's ship sailed John stood on the dock, waving, until the face he loved was a blur. Then he went to the Phoenix Foundry. They were building the engines and propeller for the *Princeton*. John was glad of that. Harry Delameter was part owner of the foundry now. When the *Princeton* succeeded, it would be a feather in that young man's cap, too.

Young as he was, Harry had a gift for getting along with his men. Often John went to the foundry to find the men in a huddle, and Harry talking something over with them. When any "expert" expressed doubts about the *Princeton*, Harry always told his men about it. "Someday," he would say, "we'll have the laugh on them, won't we?"

As the months passed, the croakers were busily croaking:

That engine would never drive the propeller of the *Princeton!*

The propeller would never drive the ship at even five knots!

The *Princeton* would never stand the recoil of a twelve-inch gun.

The government should abandon the *Princeton*, and spend its money on the ship the Stevens brothers had planned. They had offered to build an ironclad vessel, plated with four and a half inches of iron, impregnable to any gun!

So four and a half inches of armor plate would make a ship impregnable?

John was busy, shuttling between New York and Philadelphia, overseeing work in both places. But he took enough time out to settle that question.

He took his big gun to Sandy Hook. With navy men to watch, he fired a shot of two hundred and twenty-four pounds with a thirty-pound charge of powder. The shot crashed through a target made of armor plating four and a half inches thick.

"Tell your naval experts," he said, "that the Stevens battery is obsolete on the drawing board."

"How heavily must her builders plate her to protect her from that gun?"

"They'll probably have to redesign her," John said. "Plate her with enough armor to withstand this gun— and she might not float."

He went home to chew on another problem: how could he handle the recoil of this twelve-inch gun?

The *Princeton* would stand it—but what about smaller ships?

What were the conditions of success? He could not allow a four-foot recoil of the gun, that would be stopped only when the force of the recoil had spent itself. The device to stop the recoil must start working instantly; it must apply pressure continuously and evenly.

He designed a friction gear; he went again to Sandy Hook to test it; he fired the huge gun with a thirty-pound charge of powder; the friction gear stopped the recoil in sixteen inches.

"You've done it, Captain Ericsson!" the men shouted.

But John was staring into space. "There ought to be a way," he said, "to take the guesswork out of sighting this gun."

"But how?"

"I don't know—yet."

He spent long days on the firing range before he wrote to Captain Stockton:

> *I have reduced the art of gunnery to a mathematical certainty. With my new gun-sighting device, I can tell, by simple observation—no calculations needed—exactly when the gun is on target. That, too, shall be part of the equipment of the* Princeton!

Captain Stockton was delighted. He had interesting news, too, he wrote. He had designed a twelve-inch gun of his own. When it was ready, he would send it to the Phoenix Foundry to be bored and finished. There would be no need for Captain Ericsson to have another gun made on his design.

John fought down his disappointment. Why couldn't Stockton wait to put his gun on another ship? If it weren't for that one gun, everything on the *Princeton* would have been of his design—from the guns and all their gear to the propellers and the engines that would drive her. Oh, well, what was one gun compared to all the rest of the ship?

In September of 1843, almost exactly two years from the time John had started working on his second set of plans, the *Princeton* was ready for launching in Phila-delphia.

The croakers were there in full force: She would never float. If she did float, her engines would never work. Too light. Her propellers could never drive her. Too small. Any marine engineer, at one glance, could tell that the whole thing was a mistake!

The *Princeton* slid down the ways; she floated. Cap-tain Stockton exulted. "The looks on their faces! It's been worth the fight, hasn't it?"

John agreed.

The *Princeton* sailed to New York for the mounting

of her guns. The "impossible" engines and the "crazy" propellers drove her there at a lively twelve knots.

She was in the North River, waiting for her guns to be installed, when the *Great Western,* pride of England, docked after a transatlantic crossing.

"I think," John remarked, "we might give the world something to talk about."

The New York papers blazoned the news. On October 19 the *Princeton* would challenge the *Great Western* to a trial of speed!

12

Disaster

The race between the *Great Western* and the *Princeton* was set for two o'clock. By noon a crowd jammed the Battery on the southern tip of Manhattan. People pushed and shoved, but they could not dislodge a certain young man from his vantage point. Harry Delameter had been there since long before noon.

At two o'clock the *Great Western*, most famous ship in the world, came plowing down the East River. She was certainly going to make a race of it. She was using steam and sail. Every sail was spread; smoke billowed; her huge paddle wheels were turning at top speed, leaving a wake behind that covered half the river.

She passed the cheering crowds. She left the tip of Manhattan behind her. She was a quarter of a mile off the Battery by now. No sign of the *Princeton*.

Harry Delameter wet his lips and looked toward the North River. Where was the *Princeton?*

The crowd began to jeer:

"Thought this was going to be a race?"

"Where's that 'wonderful steamer' of Ericsson's?"

"Hah! Bet they changed their minds!"

"Right! Knew they'd be beaten!"

"Better to back down than to be beaten, eh?"

A red-faced man, with a voice that carried a block, summed it all up. "That Ericsson is a no-account dreamer. If there had been anything *to* his fool ideas, he'd have stayed in England. Went bankrupt there. That's the only reason he came to America. And now he's wasting our government's money. On crazy ideas the English had sense enough to turn down!"

Harry took one step toward the red-faced man. But someone shouted: "Look! There she comes!"

Harry wheeled to watch. The little *Princeton*, not half the size of her rival, was coming down the North River, against the tide. Not a sail on her spars. No billowing smoke. No churning paddle wheels. But she was coming faster and faster.

"Man alive, look at her!"

"She's going to do it!"

"She's going to overtake the *Great Western!*"

The *Princeton* did more than overtake the *Great Western*. She passed her. She sailed completely around

146

the great paddle-wheel steamer. She sailed around her again. Then, just as silently, she ghosted back to her mooring.

The red-faced man summed it all up—again: "Yes, sir! That's what I've been telling people all along! We'll beat England at her own game. We'll become mistress of the seas. Yes, sir! Because they didn't have the sense to appreciate Ericsson, and we did!"

Harry lifted his hat. "Thank you, sir. I'll tell Captain Ericsson what you said—both before and after the race. He loves a good joke."

People clustered around Harry. Did he really know Captain Ericsson? Personally?

"Sorry, ladies and gentlemen," Harry said. "I'm in a hurry. Have to get back to the Phoenix Foundry. We're working on the guns for the *Princeton*." He walked off with a bit of a swagger.

Captain Stockton's gun had arrived at the foundry to be bored and finished. Even before work had begun on it, the newspapers seemed to know all about it: The largest single piece of wrought iron in the world! It weighed ten tons!

"What's that to brag about?" John muttered. "When did a war steamer need added weight?"

Then he tried to shrug off his thoughts. He knew he was disappointed because there would be one thing on the *Princeton* that was not of his design. He forced himself to smile when he talked to the workmen about Stockton's gun. It would be interesting to watch their new friction gear handle that recoil, wouldn't it? Ten tons of iron, bucking a thirty-pound charge of powder!

Several times Captain Stockton brought visitors to the foundry to see his gun. After his second visit the workmen began to grumble:

"Where does he get all that 'I—I—I' stuff?"

"Sounds like there ain't anything *to* the *Princeton* but his gun!"

"Huh! Hear him today? '*My* ship,' he says!"

Inwardly, John sympathized with their mood. But he tried to soothe their ruffled feelings. Happy workmen were better than disgruntled ones.

"Of course Captain Stockton feels that way about the *Princeton*," he said. "He's the man who got the navy to build her. You can understand that, can't you?"

"Yes, Captain Ericsson," the men said. But they didn't smile.

In January there were remarks about Captain Stockton from other quarters—when he christened the guns on the *Princeton*.

For two years trouble had been brewing between England and the United States over the question of the Oregon boundary. Hotheaded men in America were yelling, "Fifty-four forty or fight!" But cooler men, both in England and America, were saying, "Let's talk this over." A representative of Great Britain had just come to the United States to "talk it over."

In the face of that situation Captain Stockton had christened his big gun the "Peacemaker." And—in case anybody missed the point—he had christened the Ericsson gun the "Oregon."

Some cheered his daring; others regretted his bad taste. Captain Stockton was to take the *Princeton* to Washington to show her off. The more thoughtful men in New York hoped that President Tyler would change the names of the guns.

The morning the *Princeton* was to weigh anchor for Washington, the usual crowd waited, in spite of the cold, for a glimpse of her.

John and Harry Delameter stood in the crowd, unnoticed.

"I really ought to be at the foundry," Harry said, "but the men thought I ought to be here. I believe they really wanted to march down in a body and see you off. They kept hinting."

John smiled. "They're grand fellows."

"They certainly like you! Just the other day—"

He stopped, for a murmur of excitement said the *Princeton* was coming. They could see her now—sails furled—no smoke—ghosting along as she had against the *Great Western*.

"It'll be fun," Harry whispered, "when she comes

about and sends a boat off for you. When all these people realize they have been rubbing elbows with the
man who built her!"

John chuckled. He had been thinking exactly the same
thing. Any minute now, they'd see the *Princeton* . . .

But the *Princeton* was not slowing down. She was
going on.

"What the devil?" Harry stared after her.

"Someone has slipped up," John said. "They'll realize
it in a little bit. You go along about your business. I'll
wait here."

"But I don't understand!"

"Just a slip-up," John said. "Go along."

With a troubled frown, Harry went.

John waited. A half hour passed. The *Princeton* disappeared. He went home. He did not want to face the
men at the foundry.

As soon as the *Princeton* reached Washington Captain
Stockton would send for him. Perhaps the ship would
put in at another port so Stockton could send off a
message.

All day John fidgeted about his office, from drawing
board to bookcases. Nothing could hold his attention.
That night he slept with one ear cocked, waiting for a
knock on the door.

The next day he forced himself to work. The thing he
should be doing, he told himself, was drawing up a

statement of his charges for work on the *Princeton*. Not for the patents on the screw propeller and the direct-acting engine—that would be taken care of. But charges for his two years of work as designer and consulting engineer. He must prepare an itemized statement of that. He began to collect the figures:

Two hundred and seven days at his drawing board—and a good thing he could work so fast—a hundred and thirteen days, traveling back and forth between New York and Philadelphia . . . Item after item. Even at a reasonable charge for his time, the total came to over $15,000.

Soon word of the *Princeton* began to reach New York. The amazing power of the little vessel! She had smashed her way through the ice in the Potomac! Washington was agog! Captain Stockton's name was on everybody's lips!

There was no mention of John Ericsson. No letter came inviting him to Washington.

More news of the *Princeton*. Captain Stockton had made a report on his ship to the Secretary of the Navy. President Tyler had read from that report when he addressed Congress.

The newspapers printed Captain Stockton's report; they printed President Tyler's speech. They told of the thunderous cheers over part of that speech:

. . . The Improvements in the art of war adopted on board the *Princeton* may be productive of more important results than anything that has occurred since the invention of gunpowder!

Neither Captain Stockton's report nor President Tyler's speech mentioned the name of John Ericsson.

The men at the foundry raged. They were not the only New Yorkers with something to say. The editor of *Brother Jonathan,* a weekly newspaper, wrote:

. . . We do not desire to detract from the credit to which Captain Stockton is entitled for the construction of the *Princeton.* He deserves praise for having put himself in the hands of a thoroughbred engineer, and for having acquiesced in his suggestions and followed his advice.

A remarkable result has been accomplished, manifesting a fertility of invention and a skill in construction which indicate the mind and the hand of a master in theoretical and practical mechanics. The nation is well aware to whom our Navy is indebted for this new wonder, and we should not be surprised if even Congress should some day obtain the information that Captain Stockton has withheld, in his recent report to the Secretary of the Navy.

It is a little surprising that in commending to Congress the numerous striking inventions and constructions which give this single ship her boasted advantage over entire navies, he should have omitted even to mention the name of the individual who invented, planned, and superintended the whole of them.

But official Washington still ignored the name of John Ericsson. The papers reported the splendid receptions on the *Princeton*. They told of the favorite toast on all occasions: "To the Peacemaker, the Oregon, and Captain Stockton!"

John read the reports with a mounting fury—an anger that drove him to longer and longer hours of work. He needed to work. He needed to earn money—and quickly.

Two years of his life had gone into the *Princeton*. The only money he had received was one payment on account from Captain Stockton. That sum—a little over a thousand dollars—had not repaid him for the additional expenses he had been put to over the ship.

Late in February the papers announced the most important function of all aboard the *Princeton*. On February 28 Captain Stockton would be host to the President, his cabinet, and some two hundred other dignitaries.

John crushed the paper and slammed it into the waste basket. He would read no more about the *Princeton!*

But everybody read the next news—tragic news of

disaster. The great gun, the Peacemaker, had burst, killing six men and mortally wounding others. Both the Secretary of War and the Secretary of the Navy were dead. It was the grimmest peacetime disaster in the annals of the navy. Even the report of the tragedy had praise of Captain Stockton. That gallant officer, the story said, though wounded—they did not yet know how seriously—had taken charge, quelled the panic, and managed things magnificently until he collapsed.

After a month of silence John had his first message from Stockton. A friend had written the letter for him. The gallant captain was recovering from his injuries. He had ordered that one John Ericsson should report to Washington immediately, to answer for the explosion of the Peacemaker.

John wrote and tore up three letters before he thought he could control himself enough to say what he meant to say and no more.

He would have been glad of an invitation to come to Washington a week ago. If he had been there, he would now be in possession of the facts he was supposed to answer for. He would know how the gun was loaded, the quantity and quality of the powder, the weight of the ball, its fit in the gun. These things he did not know. He could not know. He had not been there. He had not been invited.

His savage anger did slip the leash as he closed the letter:

*With the sincerest wish that Captain Stockton
may now have sufficiently recovered to bear the
fatigue of hearing you read this,*
  I am

              Yours sincerely,
                  John Ericsson

He sent the letter. He sent his bill for services on the
Princeton to the Secretary of the Navy.

"I don't expect Stockton to 'recommend' much of a fee
for use of my patents on the *Princeton,*" he told Harry,
"but the bill for my time working on the *Princeton*—
the navy will pay that. And," he added grimly, "I hope
they are quick about it."

"Sometimes they are rather slow, I think," Harry
said.

The answer came before John dared hope it would.
Harry was with him when he opened the letter. Mr.
Mason, the new Secretary of the Navy, had referred the
bill to Captain Stockton for approval. John handed the
letter to Harry.

"Hmmm . . ." was all Harry said.

By now there had been time for the first glowing reports of the *Princeton* to reach England.

Amelia wrote:

*I hope you have enjoyed your triumph, John. Are
you really ready now to "rest on success"? Will you*

be coming home soon? Shall we have the trip we planned?

Mr. Ogden wrote:

How I should have loved to be with you in the days of your triumph. Believe me, dear friend, I have been with you in spirit, saluting the man of the hour!

13

"Land of Tomorrow"

John laid aside the letters of congratulations. He'd be in a better mood to answer them when the *Princeton* bill was paid. Surely, any day now . . .

But weeks passed. Late in May—seven months after the *Princeton* had raced the *Great Western*—three months after President Tyler had praised her in his address—the Secretary of the Navy wrote again. Captain Stockton did not approve Mr. Ericsson's bill. Surely it was payment enough for John Ericsson to see his patents demonstrated on so grand a scale.

More letters had come from Amelia and Mr. Ogden. They were puzzled. Why didn't they hear? John wrote the ugly truth. The only thing he could do now, he said, was to petition Congress, in a Memorial. Perhaps Congress could see the justice of his claim. Perhaps they could understand the difference between a fee for a patent and a bill for two years of work.

The naval committee of the House did see; they voted unanimously. The claim should be paid. The naval committee of the Senate turned it down.

It was not easy to write to Amelia. John had to tell her there had been no glory and no gain in his work on the *Princeton*. He was in debt. He was going to have to work desperately hard to make up for two years of lost income. *But the United States was the place for him to do that work. He must stay.*

Amelia's answer was full of bewilderment. How could he even dream of staying in that miserable country? Surely he would come to his senses soon, and come home! When he did, she would be waiting.

That night John sat alone, staring into the darkness, remembering Mr. Ogden's words: *"It's the land of to-morrow. And you, John Ericsson, are a man of to-morrow."*

The next day he filed his declaration of intention to become a citizen of the United States. How, he wondered, would he ever make Amelia understand? Probably no one in the world would understand but Harry Delameter.

Harry listened and stared at him blankly. "I'm delighted," he said, "but how could you? After the way Stockton—"

"Stockton is just one man," John said. "You are another." He smiled. "If I weighed the two of you in the balance, you would still tip the scales in favor of the United States."

"What did your wife say?"

"Er—I haven't had time to hear." John did not admit that he had not written to her.

It was better, he decided, to let her forget about the *Princeton* claim. To wait until things were going better for him. He might never make anything out of naval vessels, but there would be dozens of merchant ships and boats wanting his propeller.

The spectacular success of the *Princeton* brought trouble in its wake. John had proved the amazing efficiency of his screw propeller. Now, every inventor of any type of screw propeller began to stir. The inventor might have done nothing but file a design with a Patent Office. His propeller might or might not be workable. But it could be the subject of a lawsuit!

Soon John found he was earning $500 in patent fees— and spending $600 in lawsuits.

How much longer could he hang on? How much longer before the governments of England and America would settle the question, once and for all?

In 1846 the Mexican War began. There was a brief flurry of talk about building twelve war steamers. John's hopes rose.

But the flurry died in nothing but talk. In 1848 the Mexican War ended. Now the United States reached from the Atlantic to the Pacific, with five thousand miles of coastline, and more thousands of miles of inland waterways.

A vast land, almost as big as all Europe, with no customs barriers, no language barriers.

John's bank account was still having its ups and downs, but he wrote Amelia the letter he had been putting off. In October, one John Ericsson, born a Swede, would become a citizen of the United States. This was his land; he hoped it would be her land, too.

It seemed forever before her answer came. John's fingers shook as he opened the letter. He read, then smiled. Amelia admitted she could not understand him. But if America was to be his country, she would try to make it her country, too. If he could send money for her passage, she would come.

The day Amelia's ship was arriving John did not lose himself in his work and forget. He was there an hour early, walking up and down, waiting. How long it had been! How, he wondered, had Bernadotte ever endured all his years alone in his adopted land?

He remembered a May morning in 1826, when he had stood on a street in Stockholm and watched Bernadotte ride by with his wife by his side.

There won't be any cheering crowds when we ride

up the street today, he thought, but I'll probably look as happy as Bernadotte did. I'll probably be grinning like a fool.

For the tenth time he looked at his watch. What was wrong? That ship was two minutes overdue already!

At last the ship docked. John searched the faces at the rail for the most beautiful one of all. He could not find her. The passengers began to disembark.

Where was she? Was she desperately ill? Were they going to carry her off on a stretcher?

The last passenger came ashore. John raced up the gangplank and hailed the purser. "I was to meet my wife! Mrs. John Ericsson!"

"Oh . . . Captain Ericsson. We have a letter for you."

It was from Amelia. She was sorry, but she could not bring herself to face America just yet. Perhaps a little later . . .

"Not bad news, I hope?" the purser asked.

"No, no. Just a little delay." Numbly, John left the ship. He walked up the street, alone in the crowd. More alone than he had ever been. Before, he had walked with hope. Now hope was gone. Amelia was never coming back.

One October day he was alone in another crowd, as he raised his right hand and swore to "support and defend the Constitution of the United States against all enemies, foreign and domestic."

A gray-haired man in a threadbare suit stood near him. His eyes were shining, but tears were running down his face.

As they turned away, John smiled and offered a handkerchief. "Here, my friend."

The man looked at him blankly. "Oh . . ." He touched his cheek, smiled at himself. "But I have a handkerchief, sir." He fished one from his pocket. "And you—you need your own."

Dumfounded, John found his own face was wet. He smiled with the man, and they walked out together.

"I'm Artur Pulaski," the thin man said.

"It's a proud name to bring to America," John told him. "There was a Casimir Pulaski who helped America win her freedom."

"Yes," Artur said quietly. "He died for her. And I, Artur Pulaski, would die for her, too."

"I, John Ericsson, hope to live for her."

"You have a proud name, too, sir. The greatest mechanical genius in the world is . . . Sir! You are that man! The man who built the *Princeton!*" Then he said musingly, "What a strange assortment America welcomed today. The day laborer and the millionaire. If you are not a millionaire, you deserve to be!"

"There's a definition of a Swede," John said. "A man born to have one million kronor and to spend two. Every time I earn a thousand, I spend fifteen hundred on a new invention." It was not the whole story, he knew, but it was true as far as it went. Not a year passed without four or five inventions—and a dozen more in process.

"I had my little metal-working shop in the Old World," Artur said. "But no freedom. Now, I do not have my shop, but I do have freedom."

"Would you like to work in the Phoenix Foundry? Where they make my propellers and engines?"

"Sir! You say that to a stranger? You are very kind."

"Men have been kind to me, a stranger," John said. "I have known a few scoundrels, and quite a few fools. But the kind men—the gentlemen—well, I still like the human race. And Harry Delameter, over at the Phoenix Foundry, is one of the best."

When they reached the foundry, they found Harry and his men in a huddle, talking something over.

Harry accepted Artur with a smile and a handshake. "Of course we have a place for you!"

Artur studied the young man. He nodded. "Yes," he said quietly, "Captain Ericsson is right. You are a fine gentleman. A credit to the human race."

A moment of silence, then the men were cheering, shaking hands with John, and slapping Artur on the back.

Artur was blinking tears. "I feel at home already."

"I've always felt that way," John said. Then his smile turned to a scowl as he noticed the casting for an engine. "I don't like the looks of that. Break it up."

Without a word two men attacked it with sledges. The casting did not crack. They grinned.

"Guess it's pretty good, Captain Ericsson. Guess we'll have to put it under the drop to break it."

John seized a sledge in one hand, whirled it over his head, and brought it down. The casting shattered. "*Now* put it under the drop," he growled. "Try to argue with me, and I'll pick one of you up and knock three others down with him!"

They grinned and cheered.

John went into the office with Harry to talk over another lawsuit about his propeller. "The more work I do," he declared, "the more money I waste on lawsuits. When will England and America settle the question?"

Two years later England settled the question in that country. The British government granted £20,000 to be divided equally among the five men who held patents for screw propellers there. That was to be the end of it. No further patent fees to anyone.

John knew his share would be £4,000—about $20,-000. He looked at his bank balance—$132.68. He wrote to Amelia:

> . . . *I shall ask that my share be turned over to you. There have been times when I could not send you much. There may be other such times. I shall always send what I can. Meantime, you shall have this.*

*I still have hopes that the United States will rule
in favor of my patent rights. If they do, I can send
you many times this amount.*

At last the United States handed down its final decision. It was even more severe than the English ruling.
The United States made no payment to anyone for use
of the screw propeller. Just gave the decision that no
inventor could collect any further patent fees.

That, John knew, was the end of any hope of profits
on his screw propeller. His thoughts turned again to his
first invention—his flame engine. An engine with fire
inside the cylinder would be much more efficient than
a steam engine. Of course he would have to build his
cylinder of a metal that would stand the heat. But surely
he could find the right metal now.

He'd do it! He'd build his flame engine . . . or was
"flame engine" the right name for it? How about "hot-
air engine"? Or "caloric engine"? That was it! He'd call
it his caloric engine!

His imagination leaped beyond the thought of small
engines to drive machines, hoists, or pumps. Why not
a ship driven by a hot-air engine—a caloric engine?
That engine would have terrific advantages at sea; no
problem of fresh water; a tremendous saving in fuel.
Of course there would be problems . . .

By the spring of 1852 he had spent months of eighteen-hour days—and $30,000—developing the engines for a caloric ship.

He got the backing—almost half a million dollars—to build the ship. Once more he made complete plans for a ship—the biggest one he had built to date—twenty-two hundred tons.

In April of 1852 they laid the keel. Five months later, to the astonishment of all, the *Ericsson*, first caloric ship, was launched. By January of 1853—just nine months after her keel was laid—the *Ericsson* was ready for her trial run.

The night before the test John could not sleep. He stared into the dark, weighing the pros and cons of his ship. The engines were expensive. Over $130,000 had gone into them already. If he decided on further improvements, more thousands would be needed.

Moreover, the engines were huge. The cylinders were fourteen feet in diameter. Would the saving in fuel offset their first cost and their size? That was the question.

The trial run was a triumph. The saving in fuel was unbelievable. Steamers of that tonnage burned fifty-eight tons of coal in twenty-four hours. The *Ericsson* burned six tons.

The *Ericsson* had not yet got up enough speed to challenge a steamer. Would more work—and more money—solve the problem?

167

They took the *Ericsson* out on another run. This time she made over ten knots. Better. Still a few problems to solve.

But John was satisfied that he could solve them if the backers of the *Ericsson* could support more experiments. He'd seen enough for the moment. He gave the signal, and they came about to return to their anchorage off Sandy Hook. John stood on the deck, smiling to himself over the smooth motion of his engines—and thinking of possible improvements.

The tornado hit so suddenly that it hurled him against a mast before he realized the wind had risen. Even as the wind clawed at him—even as he felt the *Ericsson* heel to starboard, he exulted in the strength of his ship. He had demanded they must build him the strongest ship ever built. And they had done it! The *Ericsson* would weather even this tornado.

Some workmen dashed topside, white-faced and babbling. The wind hit them, and they fought wildly for footholds, sprawled and scrambled, all the time shouting.

The ship was sinking! Water was pouring in like a river!

John shouted questions over the scream of the wind.

He got their answers in fragments and pieced them together. The men had opened the lower starboard ports, on the freight deck, to sweep out some trash.

Someone had forgotten to close them. Then the tornado hit, and the ship heeled . . .

"How long before you got them closed?" John yelled. The tornado passed as suddenly as it had struck. He was bellowing into silence.

"How long before you got them closed?" Then he felt the lurch of the deck beneath his feet, and knew the answer.

They had not closed the ports. They had panicked and fled. The *Ericsson* was sinking.

14

"Last Hope of Democracy"

A moment's carelessness—a freak storm—and half a million dollars was going down off Sandy Hook. John had faced many dark hours in his life, but this was the darkest one.

He sat in a lifeboat with his stunned partners. For a long time he did not speak. And no one spoke to him.

Word of the disaster reached New York ahead of them. A crowd had gathered. Men came toward John, took one look at his face, then moved on without speaking. He went home alone.

The next morning he met with his partners. His first words were, "I have worked out a plan for raising the *Ericsson*."

"But everyone says—after all, a ship of over two thousand tons—"

"We can raise her," he said flatly. "It's going to cost us plenty. But we can do it."

Four days later they had raised the *Ericsson*. Commodore Joseph Smith, USN, Chief of the Bureau of Docks and Yards, offered the use of the government dock in the Brooklyn Navy Yard for overhauling the ship.

"An officer and a gentleman," John told Harry. "Commodore Smith belongs to the 'sticks and strings' days of the navy. I doubt if he trusts anything but a sailing ship. He probably doesn't like steamers. The *Ericsson* must be just one more monstrosity in his eyes. But he's been a gentleman about the whole thing."

When the *Ericsson* was in dry dock, John examined the engines. They could be put in shape again—for about $12,000. He spent a long night thinking and came to a hard conclusion. The next day he talked it over with his partners. He was not satisfied, he admitted, with the present speed of the ship. Unless they could raise money —and quite a bit of it—for more experimenting, he thought the best thing was to convert the *Ericsson* to a steamer. It was the only way to get any immediate return on the half million-plus they had spent.

"But," he declared, "this idea of a caloric engine is not dead. I'll build smaller ones for industrial use. Someday I'll pay back every dollar that the *Ericsson's* engines have cost!"

Once more his days were twelve hours long, as he

built, tested, and discarded designs for small caloric engines. And he was stretching his working hours far into the night with another task.

Whatever else he worked on, the problem of a war steamer nagged at him. Years ago he had proved that the Stevens battery was obsolete on the drawing board —that four and a half inches of armor would not protect a ship from his twelve-inch gun.

But he had not come up with anything himself that could stand the fire power of the Oregon. How design a ship to meet the challenge of that gun? With enough armor to protect her, how could a ship float? Every foot of freeboard above the water line must be so heavily plated that it was impregnable to shot. And every ton of armor above the water line . . . every foot of free-board . . .

He laid down his pencil. He sat staring. *Why have all that freeboard?* He thought of his boyhood days in Sweden, his trips on rafts. He remembered his first seasick experience on a conventional vessel. "Admiral of the Rafts," the crew had called him.

A raftlike vessel would be much steadier than a standard ship. When a wave came, it would simply wash over the deck. A ship with a submerged hull could be made impregnable to shot and shell.

What about her striking power? How make her irresistible, too? If he put the guns topside, in the center

173

of the raft . . . How many would he need to sweep the horizon? If they could swivel from side to side . . .

Why not a turret? A turret that could turn completely around, so that even one gun could sweep the whole horizon? That was the answer! They did not need a broadside of guns. Just one gun that could blast a hole through the armor of any ship.

Of course, there were problems: machinery to turn the turret, to provide ventilation in the submerged hull, to drive the propellers, to . . .

Several months later he took Harry Delameter up to his office one day. "You're the first man to see this," he said, "because someday you'll build it. It's the warship of the future."

He set out three shapes of cardboard. The first was an oval box about nine inches long. The second was a box lid, longer and wider than the first, pointed at the ends, with straight sides about an inch deep. He set the box lid on the oval.

"There is the design for an impregnable hull—impregnable because it is a double one. The top hull is upside down on the bottom one. All engines and machinery will be in the bottom hull. The overhang, jutting out beyond the bottom hull, will protect everything— even anchor, propellers, and rudder. Iron plating one inch thick will protect the flat deck. Any shot striking it will simply ricochet. Iron five inches thick will protect the overhang, because it's almost submerged."

"What about the inner hull?" Harry asked.

"It will be completely submerged. To strike it, shot would have to travel at an angle under water. The force of the shot would be snubbed by the water. The overhang will protect the inner hull."

"What about fire power?" Harry asked.

John set a short tube of cardboard in the center of the deck. "A turret, plated with eight inches of iron. Absolutely impregnable. The turret will turn on a spindle set clear down on the keel. Inside, we'll mount one or two guns—but huge ones. Say two like my Oregon, unless someone comes up with something better. The turret will revolve completely. We can fire in any direction. The only chance the enemy could have to damage one of the guns would be at the moment they are run out, to fire. Then the muzzles will slide back, and port-stoppers will swing across the ports."

"How big will that turret be?" Harry asked.

"Inside diameter, about twenty feet."

"And you'd fire a twelve-inch gun in there? Man, think of the concussion!"

John exploded. "Bah! The muzzle of the gun isn't in the turrent when it's fired. It's ouside. Can't you see that?"

Harry bowed and touched his fingers to his forehead in a mock salaam. "Pardon, master."

John grinned.

"Sixty-three feet in diameter, plated with eight inches

of iron," Harry said slowly. "Man alive, how much will that turret weigh?"

"A hundred and forty tons."

Harry whistled. "Are you sure that hull will float?"

"Of course I'm sure!" John roared. "Didn't I make the calculations myself?"

Harry ducked again. "Spare my life."

John simmered down. "Then don't ask such fool questions."

Harry studied the model. "She doesn't look much like a ship, does she?"

"She's not a ship. She's not 'a home on the bounding main.' She's a fighting machine—a floating battery—impregnable and irresistible." Then he smiled. "I'll agree with you, though. She'd be anathema to any naval man in the world."

"So—what will you do with her?"

"The first time a friendly nation faces mortal peril, I'll offer to build her for that nation."

"You'll wait till then? Why?"

"Because no nation that wasn't facing mortal peril would consider her for one minute."

Harry took the model apart. He set the second hull over the first. "Right. Only a sailor in mortal peril would ever go down in that hull."

Not long after, the Crimean War started, when Russia tried to overpower Turkey, and win a passage to the Mediterranean. To everybody's surprise, France became an ally of her long-time rival, England. She entered the war against Russia.

France, John decided, was the ideal nation for his floating battery. He sent a description of it to Napoleon III. He could build his battery, John promised, in one hundred working days. It would cost less than $300,000. It could sink any ship afloat.

"Get ready to be busy," he told Harry. "You'll build the engines and propellers for me."

"How many do you think he'll order?"

"At that price? Ten at least. Twenty is more like it."

Weeks passed. Waiting, John thought, is always the hardest thing. At last the answer came. Napoleon III thanked John Ericsson for his offer. He found the idea ingenious, worthy of the celebrated name of Ericsson. But he did not feel that the battery would justify her cost; $300,000 was quite a price to pay for a vessel that would bring only one or two guns to bear on the enemy.

John shrugged, stowed the model of the floating battery in a cardboard box, and turned back to work on his caloric engine. There were still some problems to solve.

Build—test—discard—and build again. His partners

in the caloric engine had long since stopped supporting his experiments. After all, they had invested $130,000 in the engines of the *Ericsson*.

Build—test—discard. Sometimes the work stopped until John had enough money from other work to go on with it. At last he had found all the answers. He built four test engines—they cost him $18,000—but they worked perfectly.

The New York Central Railroad decided to try a caloric engine. It did the work of five men, whose combined salaries had been twenty-five dollars a day. The cost of fuel for the caloric engine? Eleven cents a day. The New York Central Railroad wanted four dozen engines, just as soon as they could be built.

A newspaper tried one for running a press. It reported "an amazing amount of work for an incredibly small amount of fuel." The word spread. Soon forty newspapers, from the *New York Evening Post* to the *Hartford Times*, were using the engines.

By now seven factories were turning out caloric engines. Men used them on sugar plantations in Louisiana and Cuba; they used them for irrigation in arid parts of Texas and California.

Europe heard of them. Even—John smiled at that— England began to order them. Thirty years after that first fiasco in London, his dream came true. John Ericsson was world famous for his caloric engine. A town in

Wisconsin even brought out a newspaper named *The Ericsson.* Its slogan was "Improve on improvements!"

The *Princeton* claim lay unheeded in some file in Washington. The model of his floating battery gathered dust in the corner of his office. He looked at that box sometimes and sighed. England and France were both building ironclad ships now. They would be helpless against his floating battery. He knew that. But he also knew that no nation would take a second look at his battery. Not unless that nation faced mortal peril.

In 1860 John realized with a shock that his own adopted land was in danger. The Union was breaking up! In December, soon after Lincoln's election, South Carolina seceded from the Union. In January, Mississippi, Florida, Alabama, Georgia, and Louisiana seceded, too. In Washington, President Buchanan seemed to be doing nothing.

At the foundry old Artur Pulaski wrung his hands. "No, no, this must not happen! Our country is the last hope of democracy. In Europe, men tried and failed. We must not fail, too. If we split the Union, we have failed. Freedom will die. It must not be!"

Harry Delameter tried to comfort the old fellow. "When President Lincoln gets to the White House, he'll straighten things out."

But Lincoln could not "straighten things out." In April, war began—North against South. The President

179

asked for seventy-five thousand volunteers to serve for three months.

The New York Times did not think they would need their volunteers so long:

> We have only to send a column of twenty-five thousand across the Potomac to Richmond . . . another column of twenty-five thousand to Cairo, seizing the cotton ports of the Mississippi, and retaining the other twenty-five thousand . . . in Washington, not because there is need for them there, but because we do not require their services elsewhere.

John watched the first volunteers flocking into New York—rowdy as schoolboys on vacation. "Do they call that an army?" he asked. "It's a rabble. An army is a trained machine. What is the President thinking of? Asking for three-month enlistments? They won't know the rudiments in three months. Harry, this is going to be the most tragic war in the history of the world."

"You're too gloomy," Harry said. "We're different over here. Wait and see what volunteers can do!"

With the first Battle of Bull Run, they did see. The untrained troops broke and ran.

"Good Lord," Harry gasped. "You were right. How long will it take us to have a real army?"

"Too long," John said.

"And meantime . . ."

"This war is going to be won—or lost—with ships," John said.

Harry looked at him, puzzled.

John spread a map. "See that—from Norfolk down the coast, and around the Gulf of Mexico to the Mississippi River? There are more than a hundred and fifty river mouths, bays, and inlets, where swift, shallow-draught vessels could land supplies. That's where we'll win—or lose—the war. We can fight the South, but I doubt if we can conquer the South and Europe, too. If England and France side with the Confederacy, it could be the end."

"You think they might?"

"The South would be a tempting morsel. Plenty of cotton to feed English mills. Very little industry to compete with them."

"I see . . . That's why Lincoln declared the blockade of the coast," Harry said.

"Declaring a blockade is one thing," John said. "Making it work is another. You know, a blockade is not even legal unless we have ships to enforce it. No nation in the world has ever tried to enforce such a blockade as this one."

"Secretary Welles is buying up ships as fast as he can."

"And not an ironclad in the lot!" John said. "Not an ironclad in our whole navy. Against an ironclad, our wooden ships will just be coffins for their crews."

"We've got some fine ships," Harry said. "The *Minne-*

sota and her sister ships—forty-five hundred tons, fifty guns. Those six ships . . ." Then he remembered. "Only five now. We had to destroy the *Merrimac* when we surrendered the Norfolk Navy Yard."

"Not an ironclad!" John repeated. He hammered the arm of his chair. "When will the Union wake up?"

But Secretary Welles continued to buy and build wooden vessels to enforce his blockade.

Then a piece of news leaked out of Norfolk that startled the Federal government. The North had not succeeded in destroying the *Merrimac*. She had burned only to the water line before she sank. The South had raised her and was turning her into an ironclad ram!

"And we haven't a ship that can stand against an ironclad!" John said. *"When will the Union move?"*

15

The Ironclad Board

In August of 1861 the Union moved—if it could be called moving. Congress voted that the navy should appoint a board to "entertain proposals" for ironclad vessels. They voted to appropriate $1,500,000 to build one or more vessels, if the ironclad board found some worthy plans.

"Here's your chance!" Harry said. "Your floating battery! It's exactly what we need; shallow draught, impregnable armor, irresistible fire power. When the ironclad board hears of that—"

"I'll wait and see who is on the ironclad board," John said. "If they have some marine engineers—or even some up-and-coming young officers . . . But mark my words! No officer over forty would listen for a minute."

He heard the names of the board and groaned. Fine old Commodore Smith—past seventy now. Commodore

Paulding—probably just as stuck fast in the past.

"Captain Davis is the third one," Harry said. "I think he might listen."

"The vote would still be two to one," John said. "It's no use to submit the plan."

But the thought of his floating battery haunted him. How could he persuade the government? Perhaps if he wrote to Lincoln . . .

He wrote the letter. He had a floating battery; it could be built quickly; it would be impregnable; armed with the new eleven-inch Dahlgren guns (John knew it was useless to mention the Oregon), and using a thirty-pound charge of powder, his battery could sink anything afloat. He could build five or six batteries for the $1,500,000 that Congress had appropriated. He would promise delivery on the first one in a hundred working days.

He sent the letter. He waited. No answer. Had the President received it? Or had it been cast aside?

Late in August Harry said, "I'm going to Washington. I'll offer the services of the Delameter Iron Works to my country." He said that name proudly. He had bought out his partner. "I'll promise the government that the Delameter Iron Works will build the finest equipment in the world, and at honest prices."

"Don't go to Washington hoping you can do anything about my battery," John said.

"I'm going to try to find out if your letter reached the President," Harry said.

"How?"

Harry's smile was rueful. "You're right. There's really nothing I can do, is there?"

Four days later John had a letter from Harry. Even though they had agreed that Harry could do nothing, John ripped the letter open:

> *I hear that the ironclad board is swamped with proposals. The time is past for submitting bids. I wonder how long it will take them to work through the mess? If only they had one marine engineer on that board.*

The time is past for submitting bids. No word from Washington about his letter to the President. The ironclad board was making its decisions now. Were they considering his letter? Would they send for him?

John never left the house unless he had to. He always left careful instructions about where to find him. Every knock on the door—every carriage wheel—the clop-clop of a hoofbeat—and he paused to listen.

By September he was berating himself. He should have taken his plan to Washington! He should have camped on the President's doorstep until he saw him! He should have . . . But it was too late now.

He picked up the dusty box that held his model of

the battery. With a sudden jerk he lifted it high to slam it to the floor.

No. The battery had not failed. *He* had failed. He should have forced the government to listen, and he had not.

On September 9 he heard a smart rap on the door. He raced down the steps from his office and flung the door wide.

A handsome young man of perhaps thirty, with quirky eyebrows over alert eyes, stood there. "Captain Ericsson, you won't know me. I'm Cornelius Bushnell. I've just come from Washington—"

"Come in, man! Come in! I've never met you, but I've certainly heard of you!"

Both sailing men and financiers knew Bushnell. He had commanded a sixty-ton schooner when he was sixteen. Before he was out of his twenties he was a well-known financier, building both railroads and ships.

He's young enough to listen! John thought. *Has he heard of the floating battery?*

Mr. Bushnell sat down, laid his long, rolled package on the floor, and grinned at John. "A week in Washington is enough to age a man ten years."

Get to the point! John wanted to yell, but he smiled, too. "Then you must have looked like a beardless youth when you got there."

Mr. Bushnell threw back his head and laughed. Then

he said, "I talked to Harry Delameter when I was in Washington. He said you were the man to see."

John's heart was hammering now. "Something to do with the ironclad board?"

"Right. They've finally finished their sittings." He grinned again and shook his head. "What a job those poor devils had. More than a hundred proposals. Everything from the size of a dory to a ship of three thousand tons."

John gripped the arms of his chair and waited.

"They finally settled on two proposals," Mr. Bushnell said. "One of them was mine." He picked up the package and spread the roll of charts. "I have the specifications here."

"Congratulations!" John said. "The other proposal?"

"In my ship, the *Galena*," Mr. Bushnell went on, "we have tried to get the maximum of protection with the minimum of weight. Instead of iron plates, we're using iron grating. As I said, Captain Ericsson, they've given me a contract. But they seemed a little worried about the buoyancy of the vessel. Harry Delameter suggested that I come to you. He said you were the one man who could give me an absolute yes or no. Will she float, or won't she?"

"And the other vessel?" John asked.

"A conventional ironclad. They're going to call her the *New Ironsides*."

"No other proposals being considered?"

"No. We'll build these two. See how they stand up under battle conditions. Then—whichever one proves to be the better ship—that's what the Union will build." His smile was frank. "Naturally, I'm hoping it'll be the *Galena*."

"So you've come to me."

"For the final word on the *Galena*. Yes, Captain Ericsson."

"If I approve—"

"We build her."

"If I say no?"

"We scrap the plans and return the contract. So, you see, Captain Ericsson, you are a one-man ironclad board. The final decision is yours." He got up and handed the plans to John. "Keep them as long as you need them," he said.

"You'll have my answer tomorrow," John promised.

"But—but—I guess Harry Delameter was right about you!" Mr. Bushnell shook hands. "Ten o'clock tomorrow all right?" He went.

Slowly John climbed the stairs to his office. He sat with his head in his hands. Then he went to his drawing board, spread the plans, and began to work.

By midnight he had completed the task. Yes, the *Galena*—ready for battle with all guns and ammunition —would float. Compared to his battery, she was a miserable makeshift. But he had not been asked to judge her. Just to say if she would float.

He was a long time getting to sleep. He awakened in a cold sweat. He had been dreaming that he had said *no* to the *Galena*. And, by some lucky circumstance— dreams could always skip over impossibilities—the iron-clad board had chosen his floating battery to replace the *Galena*. He did not go back to sleep.

On the stroke of ten Mr. Bushnell entered John's office. "Well, Captain Ericsson?"

"She'll float."

"Thank God! Then we can go ahead."

John looked at the young man. "You'd actually have scrapped the plans if I had said *no?*"

"I would!" Mr. Bushnell looked so serious he was stern. "I want to build an ironclad for the government. I know how desperately we need them. But I want us to have the best ironclads possible! No matter who builds them! Thank you, sir! Good-by." He shook hands and started for the door.

John hesitated, then made up his mind. "Mr. Bush-nell! Would you like to see the model of an ironclad that is absolutely impregnable? That can sink any ship afloat?"

"Good Lord, yes!"

John picked up the dusty box. "I wrote to the President about it. I offered to come to Washington to talk to the ironclad board. It's not the sort of thing they'd accept without an explanation.'"

"What did the President say?"

"I never heard from him. I don't know if he ever saw my letter." He opened the box. "I designed this eight years ago. I offered it to Napoleon III during the Crimean War. He found it 'very interesting,' but turned it down. The idea is this . . ."

Mr. Bushnell listened. He did not ask a single question. When John stopped talking, the young man jumped to his feet. "Captain Ericsson, the government must have this ship!"

"It's too late now."

"It can't be too late. Look, sir, I know Mr. Welles, our Secretary of the Navy. I happen to know he's in Hartford right now. If you'll trust me with this model, I'll go straight to Hartford. I'll show it to Mr. Welles myself. If *he* says the ironclad board must consider it, they will."

"You'll do that," John asked, "when you already have a contract for the *Galena?*"

"I'd do it even if I lost the contract for the *Galena!* Captain Ericsson, I'll do *anything* to save the Union! *Anything!* Will you trust me with it?"

"Take it, and God bless you."

Two days later a telegram came:

John could not remember when he had been so happy.
Perhaps not since the day he had started the first plans
for a screw-propeller warship, back in England. He
was at his drawing board until midnight. He must be
ready to get the work under way the minute the contract was signed.

Engines—turret—blowers—gun mounts—hull—deck
with overhang—he'd need at least half a dozen shops
to work on it. And they must all have detailed drawings.

Mr. Bushnell's letter was a scrawl. He had written it
on the train, and mailed it as soon as he reached Washington:

*I have a letter of introduction to President Lin-
coln. Two of my friends, John A. Griswold and
John F. Winslow, are ready to help us raise funds—
if you want some partners.*

*You should have seen Mr. Welles' face when I
told him the Union was safe, because I had found
the battery that would make us masters of the
ocean! . . .*

The next word was a telegram:

191

PRESIDENT LINCOLN DELIGHTED HAS OFFERED
TO GO BEFORE IRONCLAD BOARD WITH ME
FINAL WORD SOON

John waited for another telegram that did not come.
Instead, Mr. Bushnell brought his final word in person.
He looked as though he had not slept since John last
saw him. He sank in a chair and mopped his face.

"Washington in summer! Even in September! It
should not happen to a man!"

"How was it?" John asked.

"Glorious!"

"Go on! What did they say?"

"Commodore Smith says it's worthy of the genius of
John Ericsson."

"And Paulding?"

"He agrees."

"Davis?"

"He wanted two or three explanations in detail that
I couldn't give him. Secretary Welles wishes you'd
come to Washington. He'll have a meeting of the entire
board in his room and—"

"I'll go tonight!" John said. "And—" He was having
trouble keeping his voice steady. "I'll never forget what
you've done."

"Captain Ericsson, I said I'd do *anything* to save the
Union. I meant it."

John telegraphed Secretary Welles. The next morning he was in Washington, knocking on the Secretary's door.

Mr. Welles came outside the office to greet John. He closed the door behind him. "Captain Ericsson, I hope you'll be patient with the board. I know you have little reason to love the navy."

"You mean the matter of the *Princeton?* That's water over the dam. We have a war to win! Mr. Bushnell said he'd do *anything* to save the Union—"

"Yes . . . He's a fine young man."

"And I feel the same way," John said. He smiled.

Mr. Welles still looked troubled. "Captain Ericsson, this is going to take patience."

"And you've heard rumors that I have a temper?"

"A few."

"I've never been impatient when a man admitted his ignorance and wanted to learn. The thing that irks me is when some fool thinks he knows when he doesn't."

"Yes . . . Remember, Captain Ericsson, *we need your battery!*" He opened the door and ushered John in. "Gentlemen, Captain Ericsson!"

John shook hands with old Commodore Smith first, then with the others. He smiled. "I'm here to answer your questions. Captain Davis, I believe there was a thing or two you wanted me to explain?"

For a moment Captain Davis stared. He spoke with

cold precision. "You have been misinformed. I did not ask anything. I told Mr. Bushnell exactly what I thought of that floating battery of yours. I said, 'You may take the little thing home and worship it. It won't be idolatry, because it is in the image of nothing in the heavens above or on the earth beneath or in the waters under the earth!'"

16

The Monitor

The board has rejected his battery! Mr. Bushnell had tricked him into coming to Washington! And Secretary Welles—he was in on the scheme, too. For a moment John could hear nothing but the blood pounding in his ears.

Then he remembered Mr. Bushnell's face when he said, "I'll do *anything* to save the Union."

His anger subsided. True, they had tricked him into coming. But they had done it because they hoped that he could persuade the board to accept his battery.

You, he told himself grimly, *have your work cut out for you!* He turned to Commodore Smith. "Sir, may I know your objections to my battery?"

"It seems to me the vessel would lack stability."

"Gentlemen! She'll have more stability than any ship ever launched! In a sea that would throw an ordinary vessel on her beam ends, my battery won't roll more than . . ."

He began to explain. He had their attention. They were looking at him. They seemed to be listening. But whether he could persuade them . . .

When he finished, the members of the board put their heads together in whispered consultation. Then Commodore Paulding asked, "Captain Ericsson, would you be so kind as to come to my room at one o'clock?"

Another wait. . . . But at least Paulding was courteous about it. John thanked him, bowed, and left the room. The officers had their heads together again.

He looked at his watch. An hour and ten minutes . . . John walked thirty-five minutes away from the building, then turned and went back.

Commodore Paulding did not have an answer yet. Would Captain Ericsson please run through his explanation of the stability of the vessel again? Perhaps if he would sketch it as he talked?

John sketched on a pad as he explained.

At last Commodore Paulding smiled. "Sir, I've learned more about the stability of a vessel in these twenty minutes than I ever knew before." He got up and shook hands. "Will you come to Secretary Welles' office at four?"

Another two and a half hours. John went to his room at the hotel, tried to sleep, but could not. At four o'clock, bone-tired, hungry—he had forgotten to eat—he went back to Mr. Welles' office.

Mr. Welles was alone. "You're to build the battery, Captain Ericsson. I'll have the contract drawn up and send it after you to New York. Meantime, I wish you'd go ahead with it."

"I'm on my way!"

"How long will it take you?"

"One hundred days from date of contract!" John lifted his hand in a quick salute and dashed out.

He wired Mr. Bushnell the time of his arrival in New York. He added:

I SHOULD CHALLENGE YOU TO A DUEL BUT I WANT YOU FOR A PARTNER

Mr. Bushnell was there to meet him. John tried to glare, began to laugh, and gripped the young man's hand.

They talked long and late, drawing up their terms. Mr. Winslow and Mr. Griswold were ready to back the project.

"Among us," Mr. Bushnell said, "we can raise a hundred thousand. That ought to keep the work going until the payments from the government start coming in."

"I'll never forget what you've done!" John said.

Mr. Bushnell's eyebrows quirked. "I'll warrant that's true! Now, about the division of profits. We three—

Griswold, Winslow, and I—put up the money. You put up the brains. We divide the profits four ways."

"If there are losses?"

"There won't be. But we'll write it into the contract; we three stand the losses." He got up. "Now, I'm going to go and let you get some rest."

"I don't need rest! I'll be at my drawing board all night!"

The work on the battery was well under way before the contract arrived. John glanced through it to be sure that all figures were correct. One impregnable floating battery:

Extreme length 172 feet
Extreme breadth 41.5 feet
Depth of hold 11.5 feet
Draught 10.5 feet
Inside diameter of turret . . . thickness of armor . . . diameter of propellers . . .

Yes, everything was in order.

The payment: $275,000 in four installments of $50,000 each, less 25 per cent, and a final installment of $25,000, less 25 per cent, until the work was done and the vessel delivered.

Yes, everything . . . Then he came to an addition in the contract. Ericsson and Associates must guarantee the success of the vessel and its invulnerability. In case it failed, they must refund to the government all monies advanced during the progress of the work.

Evidently still a lot of croaking going on about the battery. John clenched his teeth. For two cents he would . . . But the work was already under way.

One hundred days from date of contract. They must deliver the battery by January 12.

John went back to his drawing board. He had no time to fight about the contract. He had no time for anything but the plans for his battery!

He had to stop work one morning. A letter arrived from Commodore Smith. John liked the old man, but he sighed as he read:

I am in great trouble from what I have recently learned, that the concussion in the turret will be so great that men cannot remain in it and work the guns. I presume you understand the subject better than I do. . . .

John wrote to explain. "Now," he muttered, "please be quiet and let me work!"

But another letter came:

. . . computations have been made by expert naval architects of the displacement of your vessel,

and the result arrived at is that she will not float with the load you propose to put on her, and if she could, she would not stand upright for want of stability. . . .

John took time to write out the explanation he had given in Washington—that he had repeated to Commodore Paulding. He proved with figures that to heel the battery a single foot, 690 men would have to stand on the very edge of the deck.

It took longer to write it than to say it. Surely, though, that would settle things once and for all!

It didn't. Three days later the Commodore was worrying about something else. The naval experts had determined that the engines would not get the required speed. If the battery did not live up to the contract, Commodore Smith would be subject to extreme mortification.

What about my "extreme mortification"? John thought. He explained in detail the size of pistons, length of stroke, pressure per square inch. Maybe that would be the end of it!

Another letter came the next day:

I have been urging the Ordnance Department to furnish guns for your battery, but the knowing ones say the guns will never be used on her. . . .

Four days later, another letter was full of dire predictions. This one ended:

> . . . *I have nothing more to say on the subject, but that the government will fall back on the contract in case of failure.*

John smiled. He was not worried about failing. Thank heaven the Commodore had no more so say!

Two days later, another letter. Evidently the Commodore had forgotten that he had no more to say. The more he thought about the battery, the more he doubted her efficiency. . . .

One letter came from Washington that John enjoyed answering. Mr. Fox, Assistant Secretary of the Navy, wondered if Captain Ericsson would like to propose a name for his battery. John would! He smiled as he answered:

> . . . *The ironclad intruder will prove a severe monitor to the leaders of the South. But there are other leaders who will be startled and admonished by the booming of the guns from the impregnable iron turret. "Downing Street" will hardly view with indifference this latest "Yankee notion," this monitor. . . . I shall propose to name the new battery* Monitor.

Mr. Fox liked the name. Commodore Smith continued to worry. His letters were not the only interruptions. Soon naval officers, used to wooden ships, began to visit the works, with endless questions and much shaking of heads.

Over and over John explained why the hull would float. Over and over he explained why the concussion would not bother the men in the turret.

One officer raised a new question. The revolving turret would rest on a ring of brass. How was Captain Ericsson going to make the ship watertight between the bottom of the turret and the brass ring?

"It won't be watertight," John said. "In a storm, when waves wash completely over the deck, there will be some seepage of water. But I have calculated just exactly how much. I have provided a pump to handle it."

The officers shook their heads.

They worried, too, about men having to live in a submerged hull. How would they get air?

"Forced draft," John said. "They'll get more fresh air than the men in the hold of a conventional ship."

They shook their heads again.

"Captain Ericsson," one officer said, "we're proud of our ships! Do you think any naval man would want to be caught dead in a thing like that?"

"I think you'll be caught dead—the lot of you—on

any wooden ship afloat," John said. "And if the government sends you poor devils out against an armored ship in a wooden hull—well—you'll have a handsome coffin. That's all."

The croakings continued. John's temper grew short. When one more officer—a Lieutenant Worden—came, John snapped at him. "Well? What do *you* want?"

"To get acquainted with my ship," Mr. Worden said. "I have asked for the privilege of commanding the *Monitor.*"

A lad who was with Mr. Worden grinned. "And I've volunteered to go along! A lot of us have. Anywhere *he's* going, we're ready to go, too. No matter what people are saying about the crazy . . ." He stopped.

John flushed. "Sorry I was so short with you, Mr. Worden. But I've had—"

"I can imagine," Mr. Worden said. "How many men will I need on my ship?"

"Forty-odd, and your officers."

The boy spoke quickly. "Great Scott! More than a hundred of us have volunteered! Please, Lieutenant Worden, remember! I was one of the first!"

"I'll do my best for you," Mr. Worden promised. He looked at John. "But there are going to have to be a lot of disappointed men."

For the first time in weeks John relaxed. He had heard nothing but gloom. The papers were full of remarks about "Ericsson's folly." But here was an officer with an oversupply of volunteers for the first crew! "I hope," he told Mr. Worden, "that we'll have plenty of time to train your crew."

The boy with Mr. Worden stiffened. "Sir, we are navy men!"

"The *Monitor* is not a conventional ship. She is a fighting machine. A complex machine."

By December, Commodore Smith was writing about another question. January 12 was the day the *Monitor* was to be delivered. He had heard from reliable sources that she would not be ready by then. If Ericsson and Associates did not live up to their contract, he would exact a heavy penalty.

John stopped the mad rush of his work long enough to explain. He and his partners had already spent over $100,000 on the *Monitor*. To date, they had not received even the first payment from the navy. They had expected to have funds to hire night gangs. If payments could be speeded up, so could the work! Would Commodore Smith please see what he could do about that?

Evidently the Commodore could do nothing. In January, when the fourth payment was due, John still had not received the first one. By now the partners had spent over $158,000. They had exhausted their resources. They had bills that must be paid.

Moreover, they were not going to meet the deadline. What now?

Not until February 19, more than a month late, did they turn the *Monitor* over to the navy. The first trial was a shambles. The crew were sailors; they weren't engineers. Even Mr. Stimers, a naval engineer and the most knowledgeable man among them, turned the gun carriages in the wrong direction and jammed them.

Moreover, the *Monitor* wasn't steering well. The officers talked of a new rudder. They had an idea . . .

"No!" John stormed. "The *Monitor* is *mine!*" Then he controlled his temper. The trouble, he said, was not the rudder. A new rudder would delay things a month. He could adjust the steering mechanism in three days. He did.

But the *Monitor* went to Brooklyn Navy Yard for a further checkup.

By now, ominous reports were coming from Hampton Roads, the six-mile-wide mouth of the James River. The Union held Fort Monroe and Newport News on the north bank. But the Confederacy held the south bank—and the Norfolk Navy Yard. Word filtered through that men were working night and day on the *Merrimac*. If she came out against the wooden vessels of the Union blockade . . . *Why wasn't the* Monitor *ready?*

On March 5—almost six weeks after the launching, the crew were stowing supplies and ammunition on the *Monitor*.

John provided Mr. Worden with some solid, wrought-iron shot. "I believe your other shot, backed by a twenty-five-pound charge of powder, will pierce the armor of the *Merrimac*. But, if they don't, use these!"

"I've received orders," Mr. Worden said, "that I must not use more than a fifteen-pound charge of powder in my guns."

"What! Those eleven-inch Dahlgrens will stand thirty pounds of powder! I'd stake my life on it!"

"I've had my orders," Mr. Worden repeated.

On Thursday, March 6, the *Monitor* weighed anchor. The *Seth Low* took her in tow, and started for Hampton Roads.

Inside the submerged hull, the crew looked at one another and tried to make jokes:

"What'd we volunteer for? Ought to have our heads examined."

"I know what got me. When the confounded thing floated. I was so surprised that I didn't know what I was doing. Before I got over the shock, I volunteered."

They scrambled to their feet when Mr. Worden entered.

"At ease, men." He sat with them.

They relaxed a little more. They went on joking:

"I know why I came. Just wanted to be a hero! If we do win a battle—"

"We're already heroes—just for coming aboard!"

They talked of the *Merrimac*, now the *Virginia*.

Though she had been renamed, they still thought of her as the *Merrimac*. She had been one of the big ones—forty-five hundred tons. Even after she was razeed almost to the water line, she was still at least thirty-five hundred tons. She'd have a crew of over three hundred. With two guns and a handful of men—not even sixty—the *Monitor* was supposed to take her on.

"Cheer up," one said. "Remember about David and Goliath? I heard Captain Ericsson talking. He said our guns, with twenty-five pounds of powder, can sink the *Merrimac* in fifteen minutes."

Mr. Worden sighed and looked at Mr. Greene, his executive officer. They went to their quarters.

"In a pinch," Mr. Greene suggested, "maybe we'll use our own judgment?"

Mr. Worden shook his head. "Orders are orders."

The next day, a storm rose. At first the men crouched lower and looked up fearfully. Then they began to grin.

"Great day in the morning! That storm is enough to throw a regular ship on her beam ends! We're hardly rolling at all."

"You know, I like a *little* more motion than this. At least enough to rock me to sleep."

Then bedlam broke out. Water was pouring in from the cable well. A slight oversight on the part of Mr. Greene. He had not seen to it that the hawsehole was properly stoppered.

They manned the pumps to keep the water under control. They were still hard at it when another leak developed. A Niagara of water was pouring down from above, between the turret and the brass ring it rested on.

Some officer at the Brooklyn Navy Yard had mistrusted the seepage of water there. He had inserted rope between the base of the turret and the brass ring. He had had to raise the turret a little to do it. Now the rope was washing out, and water was sheeting down around three-fourths of the sixty-three-foot circumference.

It turned their fires into smudge pots and disabled their blowers. The men in the engine room collapsed. The others, choking and strangling, dragged the unconscious bodies up into the turret to try to revive them.

There was no joking and laughter now.

"And this tub is supposed to fight the *Merrimac?*" one man asked.

"Don't worry," another snarled. "We ain't going to have to fight the *Merrimac*. We ain't even going to get to Hampton Roads!"

17

The Merrimac

It had been storming at Hampton Roads, but Saturday, March 8, dawned fair. The sailors on the Union ships anchored there swarmed on deck, grinned, and gulped fresh air. Blockading duty was bad enough without having to sleep in the foulness of a ship with ports and hatches closed.

They swabbed decks, polished brass, and did all the other "make-work" jobs that passed the days of blockading duty. They washed their clothes and hung them on the lower shrouds to dry. Blockading duty was a living death.

But south, across the six-mile stretch of water, was Norfolk in Confederate hands. Norfolk—where the *Merrimac* was being turned into an ironclad ram. So five Union ships swung at anchor—five of their finest: three fast, heavily-armed sailing vessels, each over

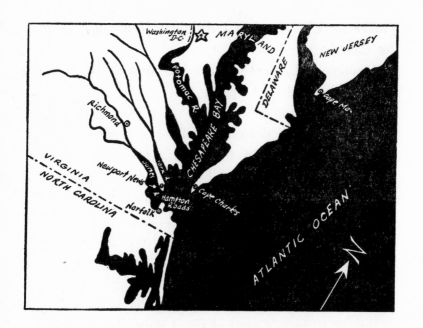

fifteen hundred tons—the *Cumberland*, the *Congress*, and the *St. Lawrence;* two steam frigates of forty-five hundred tons and fifty guns—the *Roanoke*, flagship of the squadron, and the *Minnesota*.

The *Cumberland* and the *Congress* were stationed west, off Newport News. The *Roanoke*, the *Minnesota*, and the *St. Lawrence* were east, off Fort Monroe.

In the engine room of the *Roanoke* men sweated and swore as they tried to get the engines in running condition.

"Good thing we don't have to go into action today," one man said. "We'd have to be towed to the scene."

On the *Minnesota* Lieutenant Barry watched the

"make-work" of the men and sighed. *How much longer?* he thought.

Lieutenant Lambert joined Mr. Barry. "How much longer?" he said.

Mr. Barry shrugged.

Young Tommy Wilson, clutching a spyglass, saluted and asked permission to go to the crow's-nest. Mr. Barry's eyes twinkled, but he gave permission gravely. He watched Tommy climb. "Poor lad. Homesick. Probably hopes he can spot his brothers. Bill's on the *Cumberland* and Sam's on the *Congress*."

Mr. Lambert looked west toward Newport News. "If you could see any man that far, it would be that pair. Those redheads stand out like signal flags. Six-feet-four if they're an inch. Grand chaps. I remember . . ."

He was still talking of the redheaded Wilson brothers when young Tommy scrambled down the ratlines, bug-eyed. He pointed south across the water toward Norfolk. Three steamers were rounding Sewell's Point! Two were small, but one had a smokestack bigger than the *Minnesota's!*

"That so?" Mr. Barry said casually. "So you think it's the *Merrimac?* If there is any—"

Just then signal guns boomed on the flagship.

Mr. Barry jumped. "It *is* the *Merrimac!*"

The bored "make-work" of blockading duty ended. Pipes shrilled; drums rolled; the *Minnesota* was clearing for action.

The *Merrimac* and her consorts turned northwest, toward Newport News. The *Minnesota* got her orders, slipped her cable, and started in pursuit.

"The *Merrimac's* not making more than five knots," Mr. Barry said. "We'll overhaul her easily."

But the *Minnesota* was still a mile and a half from Newport News when a sudden jolt sent men sprawling. She had run aground. She signaled for tugs to haul her off. It was hopeless. She'd be lucky if she floated with the next high tide.

The *Roanoke* and the *St. Lawrence*—both under tow—tried to reach Newport News. They did not get as far west as the *Minnesota*. Both went aground.

Helpless to go to the aid of the *Cumberland* and the *Congress*, the men on the *Minnesota* watched the *Merrimac* plowing toward her prey. What an ugly thing she was—razeed almost to the water line and plated with a sloping casemate of iron. She looked like a long mansard roof moving sluggishly through the water.

She was within range of the Union ships now. Both the *Cumberland* and the *Congress* loosed broadsides. Their shot rattled against the sloping casemate, ricocheted, and splashed into the water.

The *Merrimac* plowed on. She steamed past the *Congress*. She rammed the *Cumberland*, striking her at right angles under the forechains, then backed off.

Mr. Barry groaned. The *Cumberland* was sinking! She was going down so fast he could see her settling in the water. He could see men swarming up to her spar deck as the lower decks were awash. The *Cumberland* was doomed, but her guns were still firing.

The *Merrimac* returned the fire. Every shell left windrows of dead and dying on the crowded spar deck. The fight lasted fifteen minutes. Then water closed over the *Cumberland*. Her masts still showed. Her flag was still flying.

The *Congress* set her fore-topsail and tried to run closer inshore where the land batteries of Newport News could protect her. She went aground and was helpless. The *Merrimac* did not risk going inshore close enough to run aground also. But she did not need to. She was close enough to hurl her shells into the helpless ship.

On the *Minnesota* men cursed and prayed. There was nothing they could do to save the *Congress*. Stony-eyed, they saw her colors go down and the white flag rise.

The *Merrimac* stopped firing. The slaughter ended. The Confederates sent a tug alongside the *Congress* to take off prisoners.

"*Oh, no!*" Mr. Barry gasped. For the land batteries at Newport News had evidently not seen the white flag. They were firing on the tug. The tug pulled away. The *Merrimac* opened fire on the *Congress* again, this time with red-hot shot.

The white flag was still flying. The crew of the *Con-*

gress were leaping into the water, floundering about, scrambling into boats, clutching at spars—anything to escape the flames. The decks were littered with dead— if they were all dead.

Now the *Merrimac* turned toward the *Minnesota.* The men on the wooden ship waited. They could not doubt what their fate would be. They had seen what the iron-clad could do to a wooden ship.

But the tide was ebbing. The *Merrimac* crashed one shell into the *Minnesota,* then plowed off toward Sewell's Point.

Mr. Barry looked at Mr. Lambert. "Tomorrow . . ." he said.

Young Tommy Wilson found a hiding place and huddled there, shivering. He had seen what happened to the gun crews on the *Cumberland* and the *Congress.* Bill and Sam had been gunners.

Darkness fell. The glare of the burning *Congress* lighted Hampton Roads.

Other fires lighted other scenes all through the South that night. The word had spread. Their ironclad was invincible! She had sunk two ships of the Union squadron. Tomorrow she would finish the task. Just one ironclad—but what a ship!

She would break the blockade of Hampton Roads. She would steam up the Potomac and take Washington.

She would steam north and lay the other port cities under tribute—Philadelphia, New York, and Boston.

Nothing could stop her! She was invincible! The outcome of the war had hung in the balance. Just one ship had tipped the scales in favor of the South!

In his cabin on the *Minnesota* Captain Van Brunt held council with his officers. Two ships lost. More than two hundred and fifty men dead, including the captain of the *Congress.*

"If we don't get off at high tide," the captain said, "we'll blow up the *Minnesota.* And we'll do no halfway job of it. I'll not see her fall into rebel hands."

At nine that night—the fire on the *Congress* was still burning—the *Monitor* crossed Chesapeake Bay, cast off her tow, and signaled for a pilot.

The man who came aboard told them of the disaster.

"We're to report to the *Roanoke,*" Mr. Worden said. "Take us in."

"No, sir! Ain't going to take any vessel into Hampton Roads tonight!"

"Why not?" Mr. Worden asked. His eyes said, "*Whose side are you on?*"

The man flushed. "Look, mister! Hampton Roads is in a freakish state. Must be the way the wind has been driving the water. Everything's been going aground where it hadn't ought. I ain't taking anything into Hampton Roads tonight. Ain't never grounded a vessel in my life. Ain't going to start now."

"But we draw only ten and a half feet," Mr. Worden said. "We're built for this sort of thing!"

He could not persuade that pilot. He argued with several others before he found a man who would take them to the *Roanoke*.

On the *Roanoke* Captain John Marston received Mr. Greene, executive officer of the *Monitor*. He questioned Mr. Greene about this battery that had come to save them. He listened, nodded—and kept his thoughts to himself.

John Ericsson's mighty *Monitor* was seven hundred tons. (The *Cumberland* had been more than seventeen hundred.) Two guns on the *Monitor*. (There had been fifty guns on the *Congress*.) Fifty-eight men on the *Monitor*. (The *Merrimac* carried over three hundred.)

Captain Marston ordered the *Monitor*—seven hundred tons—to stand by the *Minnesota*—forty-five hundred tons—to protect her from the next attack of the *Merrimac*.

The *Monitor* took her station. Her crew, gray-tired from the battle to reach Hampton Roads, turned in for what sleep they could get.

After a while a thunderous boom wakened them.

The *Congress* had blown up. Then it was dark at Hampton Roads.

In Washington on Sunday morning, President Lincoln, his cabinet, and some of the naval officers were waiting for further word from Hampton Roads. So far it had been fragmentary—just that the *Merrimac* had wrecked havoc on their wooden ships.

The messenger from Hampton Roads arrived. He had more details. "The *Merrimac* rammed and sank the *Cumberland*. She . . ." He hesitated. He looked toward Commodore Smith, then away. Young Captain Joseph Smith had commanded the *Congress*. He said, "The *Congress* surrendered."

The old Commodore turned white. "Then Joe is dead."

The messenger tried to comfort him. He lied. "We can't be sure of that, sir. You don't know what it was like at Hampton Roads. The *Congress* was aground—absolutely helpless. She . . ."

"I know my son," the Commodore said. "Joe is dead. He would never surrender."

Mr. Stanton, Secretary of War, was frantic. "Gentlemen! We must make plans! I have ordered barges, loaded with stones, to be sunk in the Potomac."

The Secretary of the Navy stared at him. "You've what?" Mr. Welles asked. "We're trying to keep the Potomac open!"

"Not now!" Mr. Stanton said. "We've got to protect Washington from the *Merrimac!* We've got to protect all the port cities! I've sent telegrams to the mayors, telling them to block their harbors."

Mr. Welles stiffened. "May I suggest, Mr. Stanton, that the harbors are my responsibility?"

"What are you doing to save us from the *Merrimac?*"

"Ericsson's *Monitor* is on her way to Hampton Roads. She left New York on the sixth."

"How many guns does she carry?"

"Two. But they are—"

"Two guns!" Mr. Stanton looked his utter disgust, turned his back on the Secretary of the Navy, and said, "Mr. President, may I suggest that my orders should stand? That barges must be sunk in the Potomac?"

"Suppose we let the barges stand," the President said. "Not sink them yet. If the *Merrimac* starts up the Potomac—"

"*When* she starts up the Potomac is more like it!" Mr. Stanton looked at Mr. Welles again. "Two guns! What a threat to the *Merrimac!*"

Sunday morning at Hampton Roads tugs tried again to haul off the *Minnesota,* but she had burrowed into the mud.

From her towering sides Mr. Barry stared down . . . and down . . . at the little *Monitor.* She looked more like a floating buoy than a proper ship. "And *that's* supposed

to save us from the *Merrimac!*" he muttered. "Cheese-box on a raft!"

Suddenly pipes shrilled and drums beat to quarters. The *Merrimac* was coming! The gun crews on the *Minnesota* took their stations. When the *Merrimac* was within a mile of their ship they loosed a broadside. Their shot rattled harmlessly against the ironclad's sloping casemate. The *Merrimac* did not even hesitate. She was closing the distance between them.

Helpless and hopeless, Mr. Barry watched her. How long, he wondered, before Captain Van Brunt would order them to blow up the *Minnesota?*

"Look!" Mr. Lambert said.

The little *Monitor* was heading straight for the *Merrimac*.

The *Merrimac* loosed a blast from her forward guns —a blast that would have crashed halfway through the *Minnesota*. The shot struck the *Monitor's* turret, and ricocheted. The *Monitor* steamed even closer. Her turret was turning. Two muzzles protruded. Two shot slammed into the casemate of the *Merrimac*.

A broadside from the *Merrimac* was aimed at the *Monitor's* guns. But the instant after the *Monitor* fired, her guns disappeared and the turrent revolved. The

Merrimac's shot burst like ripe melons against the turret.

For three hours the battle raged. Time and again smoke hid both ships. Each time the smoke cleared, the *Monitor* was still there, circling the *Merrimac*, slamming another round into the casemate.

The *Merrimac* stopped firing. Now she tried to ram the *Monitor*. But the *Monitor* was no sitting duck, helpless before her approach. Time and again the little vessel glided beyond reach, then turned and fired another round.

Once she actually lay with her bow against the stern of the *Merrimac* and blasted away.

"What's the matter?" Mr. Lambert muttered. "Eleven-inch Dahlgrens, at that range, ought to sink the *Merrimac* in fifteen minutes!"

"Didn't you hear?" Mr. Barry asked. "Worden has orders not to use more than a fifteen-pound charge of powder."

"What! Of all the idiotic . . ."

"With a heavier charge," Mr. Barry said, "that would have been the end."

Then why doesn't he use it!

"Would you?" Mr. Barry asked. "Would you disobey orders and risk your guns? Remember, they are mounted side by side. If one exploded . . ."

"Look! Something's wrong!"

The *Monitor* was standing off in the shallows where

the *Merrimac* could not follow. Her turret was still. Her guns were silent.

"Maybe her gunners had to stop to bring up more ammunition," Mr. Barry said.

"Let's hope that's all that's wrong!"

Freed of the gadfly *Monitor*, the *Merrimac* turned on the *Minnesota* and loosed a volley. One shot plowed through four cabins. Another volley reaped a harvest of dead and wounded.

Mr. Barry waited in dread for the order that he knew was coming: *Prepare to abandon ship*. Then Mr. Lambert shouted and pointed toward the water.

Thank God, the *Monitor* was coming up again! The *Merrimac* abandoned the attack on the *Minnesota* and turned on the *Monitor*.

Mr. Lambert sighed with relief—then groaned. Something was wrong now! The *Monitor* was leaving the battle. She was moving very erratically. Yes, she was definitely disabled!

Hope died on the *Minnesota*. Mr. Barry heard the order: *"Stand by to abandon ship!"*

No . . . wait! The *Merrimac* was turning away. The tide was ebbing. She could not risk going aground. She was plowing off toward Sewell's Point.

Suddenly the *Monitor* came up again. She pursued the *Merrimac* and fired three more rounds. Then she gave up the chase and came alongside the *Minnesota*.

Mr. Greene, the executive officer, came aboard to report. Lieutenant Worden had been in the pilothouse when the shot struck. He had been injured, perhaps blinded.

"How many men have you lost?" the captain asked.

"None, sir. And no other injuries."

"How much damage have you sustained?"

"None, sir, except the blow on the pilothouse. We'll be ready for action tomorrow—if the *Merrimac* is. Which I doubt."

The captain canceled orders to abandon ship and destroy her. Wild cheers rose on the *Minnesota*. They spread to the *Roanoke* and the *St. Lawrence*. They spread to Newport News and Fort Monroe.

The good news sped north. The *Monitor* was invincible! She had battled the *Merrimac* to a draw! That one little ship had saved the day. She had saved the blockade of Hampton Roads. She had saved the whole blockade. Officers from England and France had seen the action that day. They would think long and hard before they tried to send any of their ships against the *Monitor!*

One little ship—but what a ship! She had saved Washington. She had saved all the northern ports. The outcome of the war had hung in the balance. The *Monitor* had tipped the scales in favor of the North!

New York City celebrated wildly. The newspapers

that had talked of "Ericsson's folly" heaped praise on him.

In all the rejoicing of the Union, only John shook his head and growled. "The *Monitor* should have sunk her in fifteen minutes!"

18

"Man of Tomorrow"

John did not cast off his gloom for a week. Then he sent for Harry. "Clear the decks for action, my boy! The government has ordered six more monitors—larger than the first one—and to be delivered as soon as possible."

"Larger? Do you think you can build them at the rate of one every three months?" Harry asked.

"I've promised to deliver the first four of them in four months. Before the end of July."

"*What!*"

"What's the matter with that?" John roared. "And don't yell at me!" Then he subsided. "These six are to carry fifteen-inch Dahlgrens that take a shot of four hundred and fifty pounds. The army has already proved that the fifteen-inch Dahlgren can be charged with sixty pounds of powder. Let's hope we don't have another fiasco like the battle of Hampton Roads!"

"Oh, come now! You can't call it a fiasco!"

"I can!" John thundered. "Get out before I throw you out!" Then he grinned. "Sit down, Harry. Now, about these engines . . ."

At Hampton Roads dignitaries by the dozen, civilian and military, swarmed to see the strange little vessel that had saved the day for the Union. Naval men of foreign countries studied the *Monitor* and wrote urgent dispatches to their governments.

The dispatches seemed to have effect. An editorial in the London *Times* spoke of that "latest Yankee notion":

> . . . *Whereas we had available for immediate purposes one hundred and forty-nine first-class warships, we have now but two, those two being the* Warrior *and the* Ironside. *There is not now a single ship in the English navy, apart from those two, which it would not be madness to trust to engage the little* Monitor.

"Wait till the next six are launched," John told Harry. "They could sink even the *Warrior*—if the navy will charge their guns! Poor Worden! I can still see his face when he told me he had orders not to use more than fifteen pounds of powder!"

"There's good news about him," Harry said. "He's

Captain Worden now, and he's going to be all right. He's already asked to command another monitor."

"Good man! . . . Let's hope the navy doesn't hamstring him with idiotic orders again. He deserves a chance to show what he can do with a monitor!"

John turned back to his drawing board. The government had ordered two large seagoing monitors. Three thousand different parts for each ship, built in dozens of different places, must fit perfectly when the ships were assembled.

Early in 1863 Captain Worden had his chance to "show what he could do with a monitor." The *Nashville*, a fast Confederate cruiser, lay in the Great Ogeechee River waiting to make a dash for the open sea. No ship could approach her anchorage without coming under fire from the guns of Fort McAllister.

Captain Worden took the monitor *Montauk* into the river. Heedless of the heavy barrage from the fort, he steamed within point-blank range of the *Nashville*, fired once, and steamed away. The heavy barrage from the fort had not damaged the *Montauk*. One round from her turreted guns had destroyed the *Nashville*.

"That," John said, "is what should have happened at Hampton Roads!"

In 1865 the tragic war ended. Almost a million men had been killed or wounded. One monitor went down, with some loss of life, when she struck a torpedo. Otherwise, three men died in battle action on monitors.

Naval and scientific writers all over the world discussed the turreted battleship.

In 1866 two seagoing American monitors gave the writers something more to discuss. The *Monadnock* sailed from New York, around Cape Horn, to California. The *Miantonomah* crossed the Atlantic and paid a courtesy call on the British fleet in the Thames.

The London *Times* summed up the reaction to the *Miantonomah*:

> . . . a portentous spectacle, a new fabric, something between a ship and a diving bell—the Romans would have called it a tortoise—almost invisible, but what there was of it ugly, at once invulnerable and irresistible, that had crossed the Atlantic safely. Round this fearsome invention were scores of ships, not all utter antiquities, but modern, and there was not one of them that the foreigner could not have sent to the bottom in five minutes, had his errand not been peaceful. There was not one of the big ships that could have avenged its companion, or saved itself from immediately sharing the same fate. In fact, the wolf was in the fold and the whole flock was at its mercy. . . .

Harry read that to his men. They cheered until the walls rattled. What had their Captain Ericsson said

about it? Had Mr. Delameter seen him lately? Odd . . .
he hadn't been in for weeks. . . .

"This can't wait!" Harry said. "I'm going to take it
to him!"

John's housekeeper opened the door to Harry. She
shook her head. Yes, Captain Ericsson was there, but
Mr. Delameter had better not bother him. "He's in one
of those sitting-and-staring spells," she said. "You know
—before he starts drawing."

"But he *must* see this!" Harry started up the stairs.

"Don't blame me if you get thrown out," she said. "I
warned you."

The door to John's office was open. Harry saw him
sitting, utterly relaxed, staring at a corner of the ceiling.
Harry paused, cleared his throat, and waited.

After fifteen minutes John stirred. "Yes, we've got to
harness the energy of the sun." He looked squarely at
Harry when he said it.

Harry entered the room. "Here's a wonderful report
on the *Miantonomah*—from the London *Times*."

"At the moment," John said, "we've got coal. But
someday it will be scarce as diamonds. That's when
we'll need to harness the energy of the sun. If I build
a collecting surface of . . ." He stared again at the ceiling.

Harry laid the newspaper on John's desk. "I'll put
it right here," he said. "It's about the *Miantonomah*."

"Of course!" John said agreeably. "Coming right away!"

Harry went back downstairs.

The housekeeper was waiting for him. "Didn't throw you out, eh?"

Harry smiled. "Didn't even know I was there."

"You were lucky."

Upstairs the sound of whistling began.

"Now he's at his drawing board," she said. "Wonder what it'll be this time?"

"We'll know someday," Harry said. "Some tomorrow . . . Mr. Ogden was right about him. He is a man of tomorrow."

Set in 12/16 Caledonia

Format by Mort Perry

Manufactured by The Haddon Craftsmen, Inc.

Published by Harper & Row, Publishers, Incorporated